Environmental Careers
The Inside Guide

Edited by: Justin Taberham, Alastair Chisholm and Helen Wilson
The Chartered Institution of Water and Environmental Management
15 John Street, London, WC1N 2EB, England
Telephone: 020 7831 3110
Fax: 020 7405 4967
Email: admin@ciwem.org.uk
Website: www.ciwem.com
Registered Charity No. 1043409

Series Editor: **Justin Taberham**

Publication Date: December 2002

GW00567345

Publishers: ADC Environment for CIWEM

ISBN: 1 870752 73 2

  ADC Environment

The environment sector in the UK has a £16 billion turnover and employs around 170,000 people. It is an exciting and diverse sector in which to work. There is continued growth globally with a market that is estimated to reach £500 billion by 2010. But the environment is not only of social and economic importance; it also provides opportunities for employment in jobs which are all about safeguarding our precious environmental assets and securing a sustainable future.

There are many challenges for young people who wish to pursue a career in the environment. The sector is diverse, with a myriad of appointments available and there are few sources of independent information where a 'newcomer' can find objective advice and guidance.

The Chartered Institution of Water and Environmental Management advocates an integrated approach to environmental affairs. Through its large network of members working in the global environmental sector, and its many partners, the Institution has gathered, in a single volume, a considerable and impressive amount of essential information. This book will be an invaluable resource to young people and others seeking an environmental career and it will be of value to employers too. The protection and enhancement of our environment depends on attracting talented people into the environmental profession, so this publication is a welcome step towards providing the necessary skill base for which future generations will, I am sure, be grateful. Therefore I could not be more pleased to support the Institution in this important initiative.

Foreword by Jim Oatridge, CIWEM President

One of the most demanding market places is the market for talent. All our organisations compete to attract, motivate and retain the best employees available. And increasingly we all play our part in developing employees who can adapt and enhance their "value" to today's constantly changing environment. We all recognise that the future depends on encouraging, supporting and helping develop young talent in an organisation. In partnership with employers and academia, CIWEM is playing its part in helping to create a sustainable multi-skilled profession aimed at improving the environment.

Investing in education and training enhances an individual's ability to succeed in the workplace. For practitioners working in the environmental sector the Institution's postgraduate Certificate and Diploma provides challenging courses. The courses draw students from the widest possible spectrum who find the experience gained from interacting and networking with people from other organisations and industries invaluable. Our aim is to ensure that aspiring graduates gain the knowledge and experience they need to enter the pool of professionals from which tomorrow's senior managers will be drawn.

I am delighted to lend my support to the launch of this careers guide.

Environmental Careers
- The Inside Guide

Contents

1. Introduction

Welcome to Environmental Careers - The Inside Guide. We set out to compile this guide because so many of our colleagues have told us that there are shortages of suitably qualified personnel in many areas. Yet environmental careers are notoriously difficult to 'break into'. There are clearly opportunities and we hope that this book will arm you with the information needed to enable you to successfully take advantage where the openings arise. It will also tell you a lot about what it's like to work in the different sectors and about the issues and day-to-day challenges you might come across in this interesting and diverse area of work.

You will see as you flick through this book that each chapter is different. There are 28 chapters on environmental careers in this book, almost all of which are written by different authors. These are real people working in real environmental jobs now, imparting the benefits of their wealth of knowledge and experience of what it's like to work in their area of expertise. They outline the skills needed for the job, the state of the sector, what you can expect to earn and where you can expect to work. This experience is invaluable for those looking to secure an environmental job and we hope that by taking this individual approach to each chapter we have maximised the level of feedback that these experts can provide. For this reason you will notice differences in language and style throughout the book. Please note that the views expressed by the various authors are not necessarily those of CIWEM.

Each of the main chapters feature personal profiles of individuals working in the field concerned. Please do take note of these. They constitute a valuable insight into the experience of others working in your area of interest. Some profile senior employees with many years of experience. Others feature younger individuals in the earlier stages of their careers. One thing is clear - there is no set route to any particular career. However, the level of experience of everyone profiled is high. If you want a job in the environment you will have to be prepared to work hard for it!

Whilst we have covered a large number of areas of the environment sector within the pages of this book, you may well find that there are some areas which we haven't covered. We have tried our best to cover all the core areas, and a large number of more peripheral ones as well. However, this book will be updated on a regular basis and we will do our best to cover any areas that are missing from this edition of the book the next time round. We also have dedicated website pages at www.environmental-careers.info where you will be able to see updates to any text in the book as well as new chapters as and when we are able to produce them. If you feel that there are aspects of the book that could be improved upon, please contact us either through the website or at CIWEM, 15 John Street, London, WC1N 2EB.

A career in the environment is likely to provide you with a varied and interesting job, which is often challenging and calls for commitment and dedication. In return, there are many rewards. Admittedly, you are unlikely to become a millionnaire, but job satisfaction is a key reason why many people come into the sector. You can get involved with shaping how society meets challenges which are unprecedented in human history. In the coming years and decades, big changes will have to be made to the way in which the human population interacts with, and cares for, the environment. The effective delivery of such changes in the future is reliant on the leadership, skill and enthusiasm of interested people like you, the reader. We hope the information contained in this guide will help you make informed decisions regarding a career in the environment. There is plenty of opportunity for you. We wish you all the best in your quest for your chosen career.

Justin Taberham, Alastair Chisholm and **Helen Wilson**

2. Supporters Page

We would like to thank all authors and supporting authors, and the following organisations and individuals for their help and support in compiling this book (in no particular order):

HRH The Prince of Wales
Environment Agency
Department for Environment, Food & Rural Affairs
Arup
Atkins
Biwater
Casella
Binnie Black & Veatch
Institute of Fisheries Management
National Centre for Volunteering
Institute of Chartered Foresters
Forestry Commission
Royal Forestry Society
Landscape Institute
Heath Hands
University of Hertfordshire
Bullen Consultants Ltd
Sussex Wildlife Trust
English Heritage
Reading Agricultural Consultants
East Ayrshire Woodlands
British Waterways
Harper Adams University College
University of Reading
Cleverly Consulting
Wardell Armstrong
Cranfield University
TXU Energy
Transport Research Laboratory
SJ Berwin
Groundwork South Tyneside
BBC News Online
ADC Environment
Inland Waterways Association
Council for Environmental Education
Concurrent Appointments

3. Finding a Job in the Environment

Anna Alston, University of Hertfordshire

Finding the right job for you in the environment doesn't differ that much from getting a job in any other field. The main difference is that it is more competitive than some other sectors and it may take longer for you to gain the skills and experience needed for a realistic chance of landing particular kinds of work. You will need patience and persistence. Each year a proportion of students who have studied environmental subjects decide against trying to use these in their careers, but instead use their degree as an entry qualification to other 'graduate' jobs. On the other hand there are many environmental graduates and others from different disciplines who have a keen interest in the environment and will be looking for related jobs. Whichever group you are in, how can you maximise your chances?

Deciding on a Job

Unless you know what you want to do, if only in very general terms, it is almost impossible to make well-prepared and targeted applications which are the key to success. As well as reading the various chapters in this book to help you decide what kind of activity or organisation you would prefer, find out where former students from your course have gone. Your university department should be able to help and the university Careers Service will have collected this information. If an organisation has recruited from your institution in the past they may be open to an approach from you.

Having made a first choice think about your fallback position - everyone needs a second or even third choice. Many people do not manage to follow a path directly from education to their ideal job. It may well be necessary to take the 'stepping stone' approach, approaching a career from an angle, sometimes several angles while accumulating skills and experience along the way which in the end will, hopefully, land you the job you really want. While your first job will not irrevocably commit you to a particular career path for the rest of your life, obviously the closer it is to what you eventually hope to do the better.

Consider taking a lower level job in the right kind of organisation: you will then be in the right place for when the right vacancy occurs, you will be known and will have proved yourself. With luck, hard work and the right attitude it is often possible to make a not-very-exciting job much bigger than it was seen to be originally. Many new graduates do not go directly into what are seen as 'graduate' level jobs, but after two or three years have found themselves working at the right level for them.

Assessing Yourself

Successful job applications result from a close match between what the employer is looking for and what the applicant has to offer, in terms of past achievement or potential for the future. How can YOU sell yourself? Firstly you need to be very clear about your particular package of KNOWLEDGE, SKILLS, EXPERIENCE and, of course, personality. Is it the right sort of job for you? (Could you succeed in the job? Would you fit in with other people?) Would you be motivated to do it? (Would you want to do it to the best of your ability?)

Knowledge

The job advert should state clearly what the advertiser is looking for in applicants. If it is a job for a newly qualified graduate then they are likely to be most interested in what you have studied, options you have chosen, your final year project and any other subjects you have studied. You don't have to tell them every module you have taken but it can be useful to give your final year programme or show that you have followed a particular pathway or stream throughout the course, for example planning or environmental law. You may have gained knowledge in other ways: through work, through attending conferences, from previous courses.

Environment-related Skills

Many jobs in the environment require you to have particular skills, including familiarity with methods, equipment or techniques. If you have done a relevant course you will most likely have gained skills such as scientific research, field survey techniques, data gathering, information gathering and report writing. Of growing importance in environmental work are cross-disciplinary abilities. Could you communicate and work with people from other disciplines, integrate knowledge from a variety of subjects, think in an interdisciplinary way and be comfortable crossing the natural/ social science divide?

If you have not studied an environmental discipline at any stage (and even if you have) think about any voluntary or paid work experience you have. For example, if you have helped conduct a survey, produced an educational pack for visitors to a nature reserve, taken part in a traffic count, taken photographs for a publication, helped write a report or driven a minibus, you may find that these skills fit the bill and give you the edge over other applicants.

Relevant Work Experience

The key point to bear in mind is that university is not the only place where learning takes place. A degree is often just the starting point and it is additional expertise that gets you the job. It is impossible to overstate the value of work experience, whether paid or unpaid, in helping to develop expertise. In the environmental sector (as in health and social work or the performing arts) it is not just the skills and knowledge you gain from work placements that count in your favour but the commitment and motivation such placements demonstrate. The biggest hurdle many graduates face is the requirement by employers that they have 2 to 3 years relevant experience before applying for even quite junior jobs. How do you gain that experience if you can't get a job? How do you break out of this chicken-and-egg situation? There are a number of options, some depending on whether you can afford not to work for money for a while.

If you have the option of a one-year sandwich placement, take it if you possibly can, even if it is unpaid. It could provide you with an invaluable year's experience (see Chapter 4). If you cannot do this, take advantage of the many voluntary opportunities around. If you are prepared to give up your weekends to pond or scrub clearance and spend a fortnight a year for four years helping with a conservation project, or if you take part in a sponsored fund-raising event or organise a recycling project, you will be showing an interest in the environment that extends way beyond what you have to do as part of a syllabus.

If you are reading this book before you go to university then try to get involved in activities to boost your experience from the word go. If you leave it until you begin to think about job applications in your final year it will be too late; work pressures may get in the way and by then you will be competing with applicants who have shown long term commitment. Check out what the employers want you to have gained from work experience and see if there is some way you could acquire this knowledge and skills via another route.

Other Skills

All jobs require you to make use of a range of skills that are not subject specific, but without which you will not be entirely successful. These skills (sometimes called 'key' or 'transferable' skills) will vary in the extent to which they are needed for a particular vacancy or within a departmental team. Employers of graduates particularly seek the following skills or competencies:

· being a team player
· ability to manage your work and time
· ability to communicate in person, in writing, on the phone and through presentations
· ability to use Information Technology (IT)
· initiative
· numeracy
· ability to work alongside all kinds of people
· ability to communicate scientific data to non-technical people

Such attributes can be developed in many ways and this is where non-related as well as relevant work experience can come into its own. If you have worked in a busy sales environment, you will have learned to deal under pressure with awkward customers. You may have chaired meetings, written memos or designed publicity posters. These are all forms of communication. If you have worked on a production line or in a warehouse, you will know about shift work and the need for everyone in the team to keep up to speed. If you have held down a routine job for a long period you will also have demonstrated 'stickability'. If you have captained a sports team you will know something about leadership, organisation and motivation.

Job Applications

The Job Advertisement

While it is possible to generalise about the skills most important for certain kinds of environmental work, the exact requirements may vary from post to post. In any case job titles can be misleading. The same role carried out in one organisation may require a very different set of attributes when performed in another setting. It is essential to study job adverts carefully and understand the messages the employer is giving out. Before deciding whether or not to reply to an advert it may help to analyse the information given under headings such as:

Job description: Does the work genuinely interest you? Does it match your needs and values?
Qualifications: Are they essential or desirable? Might they accept an alternative qualification?
Experience: Essential or desirable? What skills and abilities do you have that come close?

Personal qualities: Does it sound like your sort of place? Do the adjectives used to describe the person they want make you feel comfortable?

Location: Be realistic. Would you relocate/be prepared to travel long distances?

Salary: This is usually a good guide to the level of experience and qualifications required, but you also need to know the going rate for the job. If it is low could you actually live on it?

Any other factors: Are there any health or disability factors which could affect your chances of getting the job? The Disability Discrimination Act means that employers over a certain size must not discriminate on grounds of disability and must be prepared to make reasonable adjustments to the workplace for a disabled person. However, it is important to think about what adjustments might be necessary and not leave it to chance.

If you cannot get enough information from the advert or their literature or website, contact the advertiser to ask for further details. Unless you know what it is they are after, you won't be able to tailor-make your application to give yourself the best chance.

Application Forms

Larger organisations and public bodies tend to use application forms, which are increasingly online. The advantage of an application form is that the employer has decided what to ask you about and how much prominence they give to education, work experience etc. The challenge comes in the section included in most forms, which deals with 'competencies'. Here you will have to answer extended and multi-part questions designed to test your level of ability in teamworking, problem solving, leadership or other 'key' skills. The essentials here are to check that you have answered every part of the question, that you have given sufficient detail and that you have made it *personal* i.e. what YOU did in the situation, not what the group did.

Some application forms ask you a question relating to their business. They are not likely to want you to know more than you can find out through their website, reading their annual report and scanning the business press, but you will need to think strategically. They will almost always ask why you have applied to that organisation or for that particular function. This is your chance to demonstrate enthusiasm!

The CV

Most smaller organisations ask for applications in the form of a Curriculum Vitae (CV) and covering letter. Essentially a CV needs to be seen as a dynamic document; by all means keep a basic one on disk but you will probably need to tweak it for each job you apply for. To create a basic CV you could start by profiling your assets. List:

- all your educational and training qualifications
- ALL your jobs with responsibilities, skills gained and achievements
- spare time activities, with your involvement/responsibilities and achievements

Emphasise what it was you achieved rather than just describe the task or event. Can you quantify it? For example, can you tell them how much you raised in a sponsored event, how many weekends you spent volunteering, or by how much did your team's sales exceed the target?

Once you have a basic profile to draw on you can then decide which information under each heading is significant, fairly significant, potentially significant or unimportant for the vacancy you are applying for and re-jig it accordingly.

You will find a number of good guides to preparing a CV on the market, but the essential points to bear in mind are:
· length - not more than 2 pages
· use white or cream paper
· include only material that is relevant
· use positive, dynamic language (e.g. 'I set up' or 'I initiated' rather than 'I did' or 'I had to')
· give EVIDENCE of the skills the employer is looking for

It may take the traditional form of a reverse chronological account of your education, work etc. Or it could be skills-based i.e. contain a list of skills relevant to the job with examples of how you gained that skill under each and just brief details of dates, course, employer, and job title.

Where to Look for Jobs

You will find useful sources of information for particular sectors listed in the other chapters of this book. Vacancies covering a wide spectrum of environmental jobs appear in The Guardian, New Scientist, Nature, the Environment Post and the Countryside Jobs Service newsletter. Also check local newspapers.

What if you cannot find any advertisements to answer? It is well known that many vacancies are never advertised in the press. You might like to consider *speculative applications* to organisations which interest you. You would need to find out the name of the person who recruits for the posts that would interest you (often a departmental manager rather than the personnel department). You could write a short letter outlining why you are interested in them and the kind of work you are after, enclosing your CV. If you know that they have previously taken people from your course or university mention it. Ask them to keep your CV on file in case anything suitable comes up.

Networking is another process which can lead to the discovery of a vacancy. Initially you would speak to someone you know, telling them what kind of work you are looking for and asking for advice on how to find out more about it. This could be, for example, your tutor, someone you know through volunteering, your manager when on a placement, or someone your cousin works for. Follow up any contacts they give you, stressing that you want information and advice, rather than expecting them to offer you a job. They will probably give you other contacts and eventually, with luck and persistence, you may find yourself talking to someone who actually knows of a vacancy. It is a long shot but worth a try as the worst that can happen is that you end up with a great deal more information about the work. There is a good video available in university Careers Services on this topic, called 'Can I have a few minutes of your time?' Joining a professional body as a student or graduate member can lead to good opportunities for networking, opening doors to meetings, seminars, courses and other events where you can meet like minded people and possibly future employers!

You may want to consider signing up with a recruitment agency. The advantages here are that they may know of jobs not otherwise advertised and they will also have specialist knowledge of their sectors. Remember, though, that they cover only a small part of the job market and they are not careers advisers - you have to be clear about what you are looking for. You may also find you have to keep in touch with them regularly to remind them you are still in the market.

Don't rely on just one method of job-hunting. Many environmental vacancies are much sought-after and competition is strong. By using all the above methods you will maximise your chances.

On a final note, most environmental organisations need the services of non-environmentally trained specialists such as lawyers, accountants, human resource managers, public relations and marketing managers, conference organisers and fundraisers. Becoming qualified and experienced in one of these areas may well set you on the path to a career in the environment.

Useful websites

Careers in the Environment, Food Chain and Rural Sector
www.growing-careers.com

CharityNet
www.CharityNet.org

Connexions
www.connexions.gov.uk

Ecological Recruitment
www.eco-uk.com

ENDS Environmental Data Services
www.ends.co.uk

Environment-now
www.environment-now.co.uk

Environment Post
www.environmentpost.co.uk

The Green Directory
www.greendirectory.net

Jobs.ac.uk
www.jobs.ac.uk

Natural Environment Research Council
www.nerc.ac.uk

Nature
www.nature.com

New Scientist Jobs
www.newscientistjobs.com

Official Graduate Careers Website
www.prospects.ac.uk

University of London Careers Service
www.careers.lon.ac.uk

4. Student Placements

Bridget Fitzgerald & Lynn Schindler, University of Hertfordshire

'Wanted - Graduate with Experience'

As you begin your career in the environment sector, there are many factors which can influence your likelihood of success. Exam results, leisure activities and personal contacts can all help when looking for a job. In the early stages of your career it is helpful to consider ways in which you can meet both your own aspirations and those of an employer for whom you would like to work. Employers hope to find staff who have shown an ability to succeed in the workplace. One proven route to becoming a desirable and experienced candidate for employment is to undertake a sandwich degree.

What exactly is a sandwich degree?

A sandwich degree is a course which includes a year spent in a workplace carrying out a job relevant to your degree. Different universities may give this different names, including 'sandwich placement', 'work experience', 'year out', 'year in industry' or 'work placement'. It was traditionally polytechnics which offered sandwich degrees, but since 1992, with the demise of polytechnics and the creation of the so-called 'new' universities, the number of institutions offering sandwich degrees has increased, as the benefits of these courses are more widely recognised. The length of a placement may vary; it is most common for it to last for one year, normally the third year of a four year degree.

The benefits of undertaking a placement are varied and may not be immediately apparent. You will learn to link the theoretical knowledge gained during your studies to its practical application in the community as well as developing the technical skills which are likely to be listed on a job description. This in turn will help you learn to adapt your way of absorbing and handling information. It may also give you experience of subjects you may have only been able to study briefly on your course. As you start to identify with your new role as a professional, you will become more motivated and this will have a direct influence on your studies, with the likelihood of improving your final degree classification. Your awareness of your own strengths and weaknesses, together with your expanding knowledge of the workplace, will also help you formulate your own career plan and may help you to begin a network of contacts for future employment.

Of course, the benefits of a placement are not only felt by you, the student. Employers with vacancies will also be very aware of the advantages of hiring such students. Placements are frequently seen as a cost-effective and flexible source of labour, with students bringing in new skills and ideas as well as a fresh approach to the working environment. They can provide cover for a temporary post and ease staffing problems. They are also an excellent way of assessing potential future employees. These are points which you should try to remember when applying for placements. They will help you to focus on the requirements of the job and enable you to promote yourself in a manner which will be attractive to employers. Remember, a placement is a two-way exchange: you need the experience and the employer needs you.

What? Where?

When choosing a University, ask at Open Days about the support for placements offered by your chosen department. Once you have started your degree, take time during your first year to think about the type of placement you might be interested in doing. If possible, gain some relevant experience before your second year, for example during the summer vacation, which will enhance your curriculum vitae (CV). If you think the type of placement you are interested in may not be well paid, take some paid employment to begin saving. Voluntary work is also an excellent way of developing practical skills. Organisations such as Wildlife Trusts will always welcome volunteers, particularly those with knowledge of environmental issues.

It is during the second year that you will make applications and secure your placement. Your university may be able to help you with this. The support provided by each university varies. It may include assistance with the application process and a place such as a noticeboard where opportunities are advertised and you can find out about all sorts of different work placements.

The first step is to consider where you would like to work and what you would like to do. You should think about what the content of your course equips you to do and your personal interests and experience to date, both in the workplace and during your spare time. For example, you may be a geology student who is interested in carrying out research into volcanic activity. Your degree studies will have expanded your knowledge of geological processes and possibly allowed you to develop technical skills which will be of relevance in a research environment. Furthermore, your involvement in the exploration club at university may have given you the opportunity to practice rock-climbing, map reading and orienteering. This would put you at an advantage over other applicants who have not been able to do this. Perhaps you have language skills which would also assist you - fluency in Italian would be of real benefit if your research team has to liase with volcanologists monitoring Mount Etna.

You then need to look at what is available and evaluate how this matches your requirements. Do you wish to undertake a job where you will be working outdoors throughout the year? Do you prefer to carry out office-based tasks? Would you like a position where you are dealing with the public? Have you a strong interest in working with a large international company, or do you wish to be involved with a charitable organisation? Is it possible for you to spend a year overseas? At this stage it is vital that you are open-minded and flexible. It may be necessary for you to consider relocating during your placement year. You may decide that you can afford to consider a low-paid or unpaid placement if the job description looks very interesting. When viewing job descriptions, try to think laterally and visualise the benefits which you will gain from undertaking the specified tasks.

How?

The process of obtaining a placement is normally more formal than getting temporary or casual work. Employers looking for a placement student often advertise their vacancy at several universities as well as in newspapers etc. Students are in competition with one another and you need to sell yourself. Your application must reflect a professional approach as employers intend to recruit an individual who will take the job as seriously as they do. The first thing to do is prepare a curriculum vitae, more commonly referred to as a CV. There are many places where advice can be found about how to do this - books, web pages, university Careers Advisory Services and libraries. A CV is your opportunity to give details of courses studied at university and grades where possible, results of exams passed at school and other skills and interests. It is important that your CV is made as relevant as possible to your application and is concise and easy to read. Many jobs require applications in the form of a CV with a covering letter. Again, ensure that the letter relates to the job you are applying for.

Some companies and local authorities need an application form to be completed. Remember that information on application forms is matched against the job description and person specification. Always make sure that your application is made in the required format and by the deadline given. Some employers have a recruiting schedule and, if you know of specific companies you want to work for, you should find out whether they have such a timetable so that you do not miss their deadline.

If you do have some general ideas of where you might like to work and what you want to do, writing speculative letters introducing yourself and making suggestions about what you are able to do can be a very successful method of finding a placement.

Employers want the best person they can get for their job, but before they decide who to interview they need to know as much about you as possible. Never be shy of describing your knowledge and skills. If you don't tell them how good you are they won't know! However, do not exaggerate your abilities as it would very likely cost you the job if you were found out.

A strategic approach researching employers and organisations is to your advantage, particularly if you have very specific requirements. You may prompt an organisation that had not considered taking a placement student to do just that. Once you get an interview, use the opportunity to find out about the employer as well as selling yourself. For example, a local authority may be involved in a high profile issue such as gravel pit extraction. You can review newspapers to assess the opinion of people living in the area and be prepared to discuss the implications of this during the interview. The Careers Advisory Service at your university may offer practice interviews or have helpful videos you can borrow. Be imaginative and creative, persistent and determined. Above all, be prepared and you should get a placement where you will have an invaluable and unforgettable experience.

Working!

Remember that full-time employment is different to part-time employment. It is also different to being at university. As a full-time employee, you will have ultimate responsibility for the work you carry out, and you will also be relied upon by your colleagues to do that work properly and to meet deadlines. While most employers provide some initial induction, you will have been recruited to do some specific tasks. In most instances in the workplace, there are no extensions allowed and incomplete tasks can be quickly reassigned to a more dependable member of the team. The realisation that you are both very important and yet seemingly insignificant can be quite daunting. Some students find the transition a challenge and may struggle at the start of a placement, but a determined yet flexible attitude will help you to settle in.

It helps to remember that you and your colleagues are all working to achieve the same goals, even if there are times when this is not apparent. You should try to build a good working relationship with the other members of your team. Not only does this invariably lead to a friendly atmosphere, but it will also help you to learn more about your employer's aims and objectives and give you a sense of perspective regarding your own role.

Once you have started your placement take every opportunity that is available. Ask permission to attend as many training sessions as possible. You may have to pay for such sessions in the future, but an employer will normally have a budget to cover training. Volunteer to attend any conferences which your colleagues may be attending. You will find that they are an excellent place to meet people who work in similar organisations. Similarly, if your colleagues are writing publications, see if you can help them. You may become an acknowledged author on the paper and this will enhance your CV for the future. Don't be afraid to be brave and assertive if you see opportunities for yourself. If you are recognised as an enthusiastic and reliable employee, it is likely that you will be encouraged and given the chance to develop further.

While you are working at your placement you should keep in touch with your university by phone, e-mail and letter. Your university should act as a source of support and can also give impartial advice should you encounter any problems. It is also important to be clear about the method of assessment of your placement, particularly if it directly contributes to your final degree classification.

After your Placement

Once your placement has finished and you return to university you will spend a little while adjusting to being a student again. Some universities offer students a debriefing session where the placement can be reviewed and this allows a period of reflection on personal development. This is a very worthwhile exercise, whether undertaken formally with tutors or informally with friends. It will help you recognise how much progress you have made, and will also give you a greater awareness of your own abilities and strengths during your final year of study.

Your experience can help with your final year courses and also help you with looking for a job upon graduation. Ask your friends about their placement experiences. Would you like to work where they worked? This will expand your knowledge base of the industry and may help you when you begin to look for permanent employment. Hopefully, you will be able to maintain contact with former colleagues from your placement, particularly those with whom you made friends. In addition to maintaining an enjoyable social life, they may also keep you advised of permanent work opportunities within the company for which you could apply upon graduation.

Something Extra

If you take a look at any 'Situations Vacant' page in a newspaper, you will very quickly notice that many employers want to recruit people who have experience. Undertaking a placement provides you with an opportunity to gain experience and has the added benefit of being supported by formal studies which provide appropriate background knowledge. A full-time graduate, although equipped with a degree, will not have this 'something extra'. In an increasingly competitive job market, every individual needs to ensure they have as many positive aspects as possible which help them stand out from the crowd. Within the graduate sector, a placement can help you do just that.

Doing a placement is something that will stay with you for the rest of your career and may have life changing consequences - be warned!

Student Placement Opportunities

Organisations which offer placement opportunities include:

Arup Water
Arup Water provide a number of undergraduate summer placements and industrial placements for sandwich courses. The students gain first hand experience of an engineering consultancy and become involved in a wide range of projects, occasionally with some site experience. Projects which students have been involved with include: flood defence schemes; bids and proposals; feasibility studies; geomorphological fieldwork and support to the project teams. Gap year placements for pre-university students are also available.

Arup Water also provide subjects and mentors for industry-based projects and dissertations, for both degree and postgraduate courses. Recently these have included: a sustainability appraisal of a proposal to restore a watercourse; hydrological and hydraulic modelling of an urban river system; and undertaking a scoping study to determine the feasibility of enhancing an urban beck for a charitable community group. For further information, contact:

Mark Fletcher
Arup Water, Admiral House, Rose Wharf, 78 East Street, Leeds, LS9 8EE
Tel: 0113 242 8498
Fax: 0113 242 8573
E-mail: mark.fletcher@arup.com
www.arup.com/water

Atkins Water
Atkins Water, an engineering consultancy supporting the water and water-related environmental sector, offers a variety of student placements. For further details, please contact:

Trudy Forrester
Human Resources Administrator
Atkins Water, Woodcote Grove, Ashley Road, Epsom, KT18 5BW
Tel: 01372 726140
Fax: 01372 740055
E-mail: trudy.forrester@atkinsglobal.com
www.wsatkins.com/wsainternet/markets/water/

Country Land and Business Association (CLA)

The Country Land and Business Association is the leading organisation representing and supporting businesses of all types in rural communities, including all aspects of land use and management, tourism, services and industry. CLA is happy to offer student placements, usually on an ad hoc short-term basis. For further information, contact:

Dr Alan Woods
Director of Strategy
CLA, 16 Belgrave Square, London, SW1X 8PQ
Tel: 020 7235 0511
Fax: 020 7235 4696
E-mail: AlanW@cla.org.uk
www.cla.org.uk

Halcrow

Halcrow is an independent provider of infrastructure-based business solutions, which specialises in the transport, water and property sectors. Industrial and vacation work experience is an excellent opportunity for prospective candidates to experience working life and Halcrow projects during their degree years and build rewarding relationships which may lead to a career with Halcrow. Halcrow cannot offer every applicant a suitable placement, but does review all applications and strives to provide relevant work experience in many of its offices. Work experience is paid and competitive remuneration is provided.

Applications are welcome between September and May of each academic year and should be submitted by downloading and completing the application form on the website (details given below) and sending it to:

Jodie Curtis
Personnel Dept
Halcrow, Burderop Park, Swindon, Wiltshire, SN4 0QD
Tel: 01793 812479
E-mail: personnelbp@halcrow.com
www.halcrow.com/halcrow_studentopportunities.asp

Liz Lake Associates

Liz Lake Associates, a practice of Chartered Landscape Architects and Environmental Consultants, takes on student placements for landscape architecture. For further details, please contact:

Liz Lake
Liz Lake Associates - Chartered Landscape Architects and Environmental Consultants
William Robinson Buildings, Woodfield Terrace, Stansted Mountfitchet, Essex, CM24 8AJ
Tel: 01279 647044
Fax: 01279 813566
E-mail: liz@lizlake.com

Parliamentary Office of Science and Technology (POST)

The Parliamentary Office of Science and Technology (POST) is an Office of the two Houses of Parliament that provides independent and balanced information and analysis of public policy issues that have a basis in science and technology. One key area of POST's work is environment and sustainable development, and it is planning a major study for next year on the implications of the Water Framework Directive for water management in the UK. POST is very keen on receiving expressions of interest from students about possible placements related to this and other topics. For further information, contact:

Gary Kass
Adviser
Parliamentary Office of Science and Technology, House of Commons, 7 Millbank, London, SW1P 3JA
Tel: 020 7219 2161
Fax: 020 7219 2849
E-mail: kassg@parliament.uk
www.parliament.uk/post/home.htm

Peter Brett Associates
Peter Brett Associates, consulting engineers with a water and environment department, offers work and industrial placements to students in addition to sponsorship schemes. Please contact:

Brian Allen - Technical Services Manager / Felicity Warren - Recruitment and Training Manager
Peter Brett Associates, 16 Westcote Road, Reading, RG30 2DE
Tel: 01189500761
Fax: 01189597498
E-mail: ballen@pba.co.uk
www.pba.co.uk

5. Volunteering: Another Route to a Career

Roberta de Joia, Heath Hands

We are grateful to the National Centre for Volunteering for kindly allowing use of information from their website in this chapter.

You may be ready for that first job, but is that first job out there waiting for you?

It may be just a quirk of fate, bad luck or 'sod's law', but getting started in a career is rarely easy. You scour the adverts only to learn that most jobs demand experience, even the lowliest, financially challenged ones. The nightmare scenario might go like this:

You've got your qualifications and did very well, thank you. You've completed your training and you're raring to go. But every job advert asks for people with experience and your CV stops abruptly after the section on Education. You know you could do the job if only you could get a look in, but your CV looks much the same as thousands of others. How to make it stand out?

The answer could lie with volunteering.

Or you may be set to start out, but are not quite sure which aspect of environmental work you want to work in. Are you looking for hands-on outdoor work or are you a computer lover and more suited to admin work, dealing with policy, strategy or planning? You want to have a go at more than one aspect of work, but can't quite figure out how to go about it?

Again, the answer could lie with volunteering.

And volunteering is the ideal gap year or between-jobs activity that can keep you connected to the world of work. Apart from any benefits for you and for the organisation looking for volunteers, volunteering is sure-fire first aid for an ailing CV.

At Heath Hands, the volunteer corps for Hampstead Heath in North London, for example, it is clear that those working for *free* are not working for *nothing* because volunteering pays its own dividends, primarily by filling gaps in the CV for younger members and filling gaps in breadth of experience for those already on the career ladder.

One young geography graduate popped in to the office to join Heath Hands because she needed something other than student activity on her CV. She soon discovered that the computing and organising skills she had acquired as an undergraduate were just what the organisation needed. So after applying unsuccessfully for many jobs, she found herself with her first real job and with a foot firmly planted on a career ladder. In the end, she combined volunteering outdoors with paid employment actually organising the outdoor work. Another young graduate, who had spent several years in dead-end office jobs, found that her well-honed admin skills, coupled with a new commitment to outdoor volunteering, landed her the job she had always wanted with the Environment Agency.

One of our other success stories was a young designer, fresh out of uni, who volunteered to design and put together the Heath Hands newsletter, *Hands Update*. Her newly enhanced CV, together with samples of her now published work, landed her the graphic design job she wanted. Her new boss commented: "If you are willing to work for free, I'm convinced that you really want to work." What better endorsement of volunteering can you get?

Everyone who joins Heath Hands is expected to do their bit with litter picking, helping to manage clearance of invasive species, clearing ditches, repairing paths, painting benches, and a host of other normally mundane and repetitive tasks. The thing is, though, that when you are doing a repetitive task with other like-minded people of any age, it is genuinely fun. A bonus is the camaraderie that develops among people who enjoy getting out together. It becomes a stress-free environment; there are no exams and the activity is designed for beginners, with plenty of help around to show the inexperienced how to wield the secateurs, scythe or mattock and how to tell a sycamore from an oak.

The very act of joining a new group gives you a leg up in the job stakes because word gets around that you're looking. Those who take in just why we do what we do immediately enhance their understanding, improve their CVs and often move towards a career in the environment. Within a few months, many volunteers find themselves engaged in policy matters involving open spaces management, identifying flora and fauna, learning about the ecology and historical aspects of the sites on which we work, as well as helping to run the organisation itself.

So let's assume that you want to volunteer. How do you find out about the opportunities? Most people want to volunteer for work within easy commuting distance of their homes, so you need to know how to go about volunteer job hunting in or near your own community.

If your community has a Volunteer Bureau, that is the ideal place to begin. Bureaux all over the country keep lists of volunteer opportunities and can help link you to an appropriate organisation. Councils for Voluntary Service often act as a volunteer bureau if there is no local bureau. But if you cannot track down your nearest Volunteer Bureau or Council for Voluntary Service or there isn't one near enough, then your best bet is to log on to the superb website of the National Centre for Volunteering. Their information on environmental and conservation volunteering can be found at: www.volunteering.org.uk/volunteer/environmentconserve.htm

And the first listing is for the largest practical conservation charity in the country: the British Trust for Conservation Volunteers (BTCV), which actually involves some 130,000 volunteers annually in environmental projects. They offer one-day projects, working holidays, international community development work and short courses. BTCV also arranges placements for Millennium Volunteers, aimed specifically at helping unemployed people between the ages of 16 and 24.

The site is a mine of information, with listings for all the well-known national groups: The Tidy Britain Group, Friends of the Earth, National Trust, Greenpeace, Sustrans, Federation of City Farms and Community Gardens, and Groundwork. Their contact details are listed at the end of this chapter. The site provides links to all these and many more, giving a rundown on what each organisation does and how to contact them. In short, there are thousands of volunteer opportunities, any one of which could be the opportunity to work in a field of your choice.

Once you have found something of interest, ring, write or e-mail the organisation you are interested in to find out exactly how to join. Some organisations are more bureaucratic than others and may ask you to fill in a proper application form and attend an informal interview. The point is to make sure that you can do the job they need doing and that you in turn will find the work helpful and satisfying. So don't cringe at the thought of an interview.

Other organisations, like Heath Hands, for example, bill themselves as 'open membership' organisations which means that anyone can join. We do, however, expect those who do join to commit themselves to 18 hours a year of volunteer work. Not a lot; most people do much more. You will also have to check out what other commitments there might be. Will you have to supply your own protective clothing?

At Heath Hands, the Corporation of London, manager of Hampstead Heath, supplies all our protective clothing including t-shirts, sweatshirts, gloves and steel-capped boots (all of which we get to keep) and the hand tools for the job (which we don't keep). They also provide professional supervision for all our work so that every job becomes a worthwhile learning experience.

And that is just for starters. What delights most members is that apart from gaining skills and knowledge, they also gain new friends and some amazing contacts in the fields they wish to become involved with in their careers. And don't forget the feel-good factor. Few things can be as rewarding as seeing a job well done.

Heath Hands can be contacted at:
Heath Hands, The Iveagh Bequest, Kenwood, Hampstead Lane, London, NW3 7JR
Tel: 020 8458 9102
E-mail: info@heath-hands.org.uk
www.heath-hands.org.uk

Contacts provided by the National Centre for Volunteering

As noted, the National Centre for Volunteering is an excellent source of information on volunteering. The Centre also produces a joint publication with TimeBank for people who want to volunteer. This useful 44-page guide includes ideas, opportunities and contacts, plus some basic practical advice and volunteers' own experiences. Check the website to find out how to obtain your free copy.

National Centre for Volunteering, Regent's Wharf, 8 All Saints Street,
London, N1 9RL
Tel: 020 7520 8900
E-mail: volunteering@thecentre.org.uk
www.volunteering.org.uk

We are grateful to the National Centre for Volunteering for kindly allowing use of the following information from their website.

British Trust for Conservation Volunteers (BTCV)
This is the UK's largest practical conservation charity, annually involving 130,000 volunteers in projects to protect and enhance the environment. The organisation offers one-day conservation projects, international conservation working holidays, international community development work, courses and vocational training,

Millennium Volunteers placements and training for the unemployed.
BTCV, 36 St Mary's Street, Wallingford, Oxfordshire OX10 0EU
Tel: 01491 821600
E-mail: Information@btcv.org.uk
www.btcv.org.uk

Do-it.org.uk (YouthNet UK)
A useful internet database of UK local volunteering opportunities, which is searchable by postcode, type of work and type of organisation. It also includes some information about overseas volunteering.
www.do-it.org.uk

Federation of City Farms and Community Gardens
City Farms and Community Gardens are locally based projects working with people, animals and plants. Each one is unique. They are (or are aiming to become) community-led and managed, empowering those involved through a sustainable approach to what they do. Many City Farms and Community Gardens are dependent on volunteers for their survival and development, as they often only have a few, if any, paid staff. For a list of local city farms contact:
The Green House, Hereford Street, Bristol, BS3 4NA
Tel: 0117 9231 800
E-mail: admin@farmgarden.org.uk
www.farmgarden.org.uk

Friends of the Earth
Friends of the Earth (FOE) campaigns for the protection of the environment and proposes alternatives to environmentally damaging policies and practices. It provides authoritative information and lobbies to change official policy. As well as a National Office FOE has regional offices and a network of over 250 local groups, all of which rely on volunteer help.
Friends of the Earth, 26-28 Underwood Street, London, N1 7JQ
Tel: 020 7490 1555
E-mail: info@foe.co.uk
www.foe.co.uk

Greenpeace
Greenpeace is an international, independent campaigning organisation, using non-violent direct action for industrial and political solutions to prevent abuse of the natural world. A network of campaign support groups help to publicise campaigning issues.
Greenpeace, Canonbury Villas, London, N1 2PN
Tel: 020 7865 8100
E-mail: info@uk.greenpeace.org
www.greenpeace.org.uk

Groundwork (formerly Groundwork Foundation)
Groundwork is a leading environmental regeneration charity. From small community schemes to major regional and national programmes, their network of over 40 local Trusts works in partnership with local people, local authorities and business to promote economic and social regeneration by improvements to the local environment. The local Trusts involve volunteers in their work.
Groundwork, 85-87 Cornwall Street, Birmingham, B3 3BY
Tel: 0121 236 8565

E-mail: info@groundwork.org.uk
www.groundwork.org.uk

The National Trust
The National Trust conserves many of Britain's historical buildings and landscapes for the benefit of the nation. Volunteers are active and welcome at every level of the Trust, including working holidays. The Trust's Volunteering and Community Involvement Office can put you in touch with the regional offices, which link people with volunteering opportunities at Trust properties. Details of regional offices can also be found on the website.
The Volunteering & Community Involvement Office, National Trust, 33 Sheep St, Cirencester, Gloucestershire, GL7 1RQ
Tel: 01285 651818
E-mail: xeajch@smtp.ntrust.org.uk
www.nationaltrust.org.uk/volunteers

Sustrans
Sustrans is the sustainable transport charity which coordinated the development of the National Cycle Network. It needs Volunteer Rangers in most parts of the UK to help to monitor and look after sections of route near their homes. Rangers play a vital role to help keep routes safe and attractive for users.
Volunteer Ranger Team, Sustrans, 35 King Street, Bristol, BS1 4DZ
Tel: 0117 915 0100
E-mail: rangers-uk@sustrans.org.uk
www.sustrans.org.uk

The Tidy Britain Group
The Group works to improve local environments. It runs campaigns, educational programmes, advisory services and award schemes aimed at getting all sectors of society involved in clearing up litter. Volunteers can get involved in the Britain in Bloom competition and campaigns like the 'Just Bin It' nationwide litter action, Roadside Care and the Countryside initiative.
Tidy Britain Group, Elizabeth House, The Pier, Wigan, WN3 4EX
Tel: 01942 824620
E-mail: tidy.britain@virgin.net
www.tidybritain.org.uk

Other Contacts

Royal Society for the Protection of Birds (RSPB)
RSPB benefits from a wide range of people in volunteer positions. Check the vacancy search on the website to find the opportunity best suited to you.
RSPB UK Headquarters, The Lodge, Sandy, Bedfordshire, SG19 2DL
Tel: 01767 680551
www.rspb.org.uk

Wildlife Trusts
The nationwide Wildlife Trusts have 23,800 regular volunteers, with a huge range of activities to suit all interests, including "hands-on" conservation, working in visitor centres and shops, working with children through Wildlife Watch and fundraising. Wildlife Trusts also need help from those with skills in photography, illustration, accountancy, public relations, and administration - the list is endless. To find out more about your local Wildlife Trust, contact:
The Wildlife Trusts, The Kiln, Waterside, Mather Road,

Newark, Nottinghamshire, NG241WT
Tel: 0870 036 7711; Fax: 0870 036 0101
E-mail: info@wildlife-trusts.cix.co.uk
www.wildlifetrusts.org

Overseas Volunteering

Earthwatch
57 Woodstock Rd, Oxford, OX2 6HJ
Tel: 01865 318838; Fax: 01865 311383
E-mail: info@earthwatch.org.uk
www.earthwatch.org/europe

Voluntary Service Overseas (VSO)
317 Putney Bridge Road, London, SW15 2PN
Telephone: 020 8780 7200; Fax: 020 8780 7300
E-mail: enquiry@vso.org.uk
www.vso.org.uk

Raleigh International
27 Parsons Green Lane, London, SW6 4HZ
Tel: 0207 371 8585; Fax: 0207 371 5116
E-mail: international@raleigh.org.uk
www.raleigh.org.uk

Publications

The Guardian newspaper features an interesting selection of volunteering opportunities. These appear most Wednesdays in the jobs section. *Local press* may also have articles about voluntary work.

There are several published *directories of voluntary work*, and most libraries will have at least one of these in the reference or careers section. 'The Voluntary Agencies Directory' is particularly useful if you know exactly what you want to do as it has an excellent index of types of organisation. Public libraries may also have a noticeboard or a file of information on voluntary work.

6. Environmental Education

Ewan McLeish, Independent Environmental Education Consultant

The Sector

Environmental education is a rapidly evolving field that has changed and broadened in scope in recent years. Since the Earth Summit in Rio in 1992, the term Education for Sustainable Development (ESD) has come into common usage, reflecting the need to address environmental and conservation issues within a broader economic, social and political context. This involves concepts such as the interdependence of society, economy and the natural environment, citizenship and stewardship, the importance of cultural and economic as well as biological diversity, and issues to do with quality of life, equity and justice. To reflect this, the terms Environmental Education and ESD have been used jointly in this chapter i.e. environmental education/ESD.

While ideas about environmental education have changed, the underlying aims remain the same. A recent definition given in the First Annual Report of the Sustainable Development Education Panel (Department of the Environment, Transport and the Regions, 1998) emphasises the dynamic and participative approach that is central to the education process:

"Education for sustainable development enables people to develop the knowledge, values and skills to participate in decisions about the way we do things individually and collectively, both locally and globally, that will improve the quality of life now without damaging the planet for the future."

If people are to be sympathetic towards conservation and environmental goals, they need to both understand, and be able to relate to, the issues involved. Education has a vital role to play in this process.

Sector Profile

Environmental education/ESD takes place in many different situations and it is therefore difficult to estimate exact numbers of people involved. For example, many teachers are involved in environmental education/ESD but few, if any, will have this as their main job description or title. Most of the major conservation organisations employ one or, increasingly, a team of education staff. Local authorities are also increasingly taking on staff to work on environment and sustainable development issues with schools and other education establishments, or more generally in the community. There are also large numbers of volunteers involved in the field.

A conservative estimate would suggest there are around 20,000 to 30,000 people involved, either full or part-time, in environmental education/ESD in the UK. Many of these will be teachers, however, for whom environmental education will not be a main responsibility. Similarly, local authority officers, say in waste or parks departments, may have education as part of their overall remit. Full time professionals probably lie in the region of 3000 to 5000. The sector is currently growing, however, as the need to engage people in the environmental debate becomes more urgent, and the field itself becomes broader.

Typical Post Names

Education Officer, Information Officer, Field Study Officer, Head of Education, Head of Centre, Policy Development Officer (Education), Community Development Officer

Main Employers

- Voluntary sector organisations e.g. RSPB, Wildlife Trusts, National Trust
- Government agencies e.g. Environment Agency, English Nature
- Large utilities e.g. water companies, energy companies
- Local authorities e.g. field and outdoor centre staff, Local Agenda 21/ Community Strategy Officers
- Science and other centres e.g. Eden Project, botanic gardens, commercial outdoor centres, Sea Life Centres
- Many schools will have a teacher responsible for environmental education/ ESD and this may or may not be a scale post.
- There is a small, but increasing, number of consultants in the field.

Career Opportunities

Many people in the field are former teachers who have been involved in environmental education/ESD as part of their duties in school, but wish to devote themselves to environmental education full time. They will obviously have both teaching qualifications and considerable experience of the education sector.

Experience in education is particularly important. Working with schools, youth organisations or more generally in the community requires a good understanding of how education works, how people learn and how they can become involved. It is not enough to be knowledgeable or enthusiastic about the subject since this can actually alienate people who may not share the same concerns or priorities. Providing a successful education experience is a complex process that needs to be properly targeted, meticulously planned, professionally carried out and then evaluated against the aims for which it was devised.

This does not necessarily mean you need formal teaching qualifications (although some jobs may require this). For example, qualifications in outdoor education, youth work, or community development may be equally appropriate. A good track record of voluntary work also counts for a great deal, but a thorough understanding of the education *process* is a fundamental requirement.

There are a small number of courses, mainly run by higher education institutions, specifically aimed at those wishing to pursue a career in environmental education/ ESD. These are normally post-graduate courses and may be full or part-time. Some teacher-training establishments have a strong environmental strand to their training and it is worth studying the prospectuses or making specific enquiries when applying for courses.

Salaries obviously vary with experience and qualifications. As with most other environmentally-orientated careers, this is not normally a pathway to wealth and fame. But it can be an intensely rewarding experience knowing that you may be responsible for changing people's attitudes towards the environment for life.

The salary for a 'typical' education post for a graduate with previous education experience might be expected to be in the region of £15,000 to £18,500, less for junior posts and obviously more for experienced professionals. A senior post in a large organisation, with responsibility for policy development and a number of staff, can be reasonably well-rewarded, certainly in the £35,000 to £45,000 region, and sometimes more.

Public sector
Although all levels of government and some government agencies support environmental education/ESD, most posts are found at local authority level. Education authorities may run environmental centres of various kinds although these are increasingly being run privately or in partnership with the voluntary or commercial sector.

A noticeable trend has been for a variety of local authority departments, other than education, such as planning or environmental services, to employ education staff. With the development and implementation of Local Agenda 21 and, more, recently, Community Strategies, there are many opportunities to work in a broadly educational context. This may involve working with local communities to develop ways in which they can reduce their environmental impact, as well as improving (and enjoying) their local environment.

Private sector
Many of the larger commercial sector organisations employ their own education staff. They are often involved in the development of educational material or running projects with schools. Some companies, particularly the utilities, run their own centres since they often have access to large amounts of land, some of which supports interesting habitats.

Private sector organisations also work collaboratively with voluntary sector (non-profit) organisations and with local authorities. For example, they may fund the salaries of staff in an authority-run field centre or a wildlife trust. They may also sponsor education programmes run by the voluntary sector.

Non-profit sector
This is probably the largest single sector employer. Most environmental organisations recognise the need to support their work with a strong education presence, although this can sometimes lead to competitive, rather than collaborative, approaches. Traditionally, education has been the poor relation within the conservation/environmental field, but its increasing profile, for example in the National Curriculum and post-16 qualifications, means that it is now being addressed more seriously.

Traditionally too, the voluntary sector has tended to be the poorest payer and the slowest to address other aspects of employment such as contracts, working conditions and pensions. Once again, however, there is a greater recognition of the need to attract high-calibre candidates and offer similar conditions to those in, say, the public sector. Against this, the rise of lottery funding means that posts may be for a fixed period only and have no guarantee of being continued. Similarly, the small size of many of these organisations may mean there is no clear career development pathway.

Issues and Trends

As already indicated, the most significant trend has been the broadening of environmental education to encompass ideas about sustainable development. This has meant new approaches being developed and new collaborations being forged.

For example, the links between health and environmental issues are now well recognised and this is reflected in initiatives such as Healthy Schools, which has a strong environmental component. Similarly the development education and environmental education movements have come closer together, recognising their common aims while benefiting from their different experiences, approaches and constituencies.

In the formal education sector, Education for Sustainable Development (ESD) is now higher up the education pecking order than ever, being recognised as a significant and statutory element of the National Curriculum (this has not always been backed by resources however!). The non-statutory, but influential, Schemes of Work produced for teachers by the Qualifications and Curriculum Agency (QCA) also contain much excellent ESD content, and this is currently being enhanced. The QCA runs its own website dedicated to ESD (see the Websites section at the end of the chapter for details) and this is well-worth visiting to get an overview of developments and current ideas in relation to the school curriculum.

There has, perhaps, been a tendency for environmental education/ESD organisations to target schools to the exclusion of other sectors, such as the youth service or the community generally. This is now being partly addressed through the greater recognition of schools as part of the wider community from which they draw and with which they interact, not only in terms of parents, pupils and staff, but also in terms of resources and services. The idea of sustainable schools as part of sustainable communities is now taking hold. Nevertheless, there is a need for more specialists to work in a more targeted way with groups that are sometimes excluded from traditional education programmes, such as ethnic minorities and young men.

The ability to gain access, via the Internet, to enormous amounts of information and a huge range of educational resources also poses new opportunities as well as challenges. Networking between schools, for example, both in the UK and internationally, has allowed the rich exchange of data, information and views between young people all over the world. Sharing local issues and concerns across different continents and different cultures may do much to make those issues more understandable and, ultimately, more resolvable.

Environmental education/ESD is a vital part of moving towards a more sustainable world. There are reasonable job opportunities and the work can be immensely satisfying. Like many jobs in conservation and the environment, however, it is a vocation and not a soft option. It is intellectually demanding and you will be constantly reviewing what you have achieved. Educational benefits are often only realised in the long term. This can be discouraging at times and may force organisations with tight budgets and impatient sponsors to go down well-trodden, rather than innovative, paths. In the end, however, the challenges you face will be the ones you set yourself.

Personal Profiles

Christiane Dorion - Senior Education Officer, WWF-UK

"I was born in Québec and spent summers fishing, camping and canoeing. Having family in Europe, we also spent our holidays travelling in a campervan from Paris to Istanbul. These experiences of outdoor life and travelling definitely influenced my decision to read geography at university.

After completing my first degree, I was offered a lecturing post at Laval University, introducing teacher trainees to geography, history and social studies. I also had the opportunity to work with primary schools on the implementation of the Québec national curriculum and the development of teaching resources. Whilst in this post, I completed a Masters Degree in Education in order to pursue my career at the university.

In 1985, I travelled in China for two months and this experience encouraged me to develop my career abroad. Back in Canada, I obtained a scholarship from the Québec government to carry out a PhD in the UK, where child-centred teaching strategies were very strong. This also provided me with an opportunity to learn English!

My thesis focused on environmental education and I was able to visit many primary schools with excellent environmental education practice and strong policies. After completing my PhD, I was asked to contribute to the development of environmental education guidelines for the National Curriculum for England and Wales. I then worked for the Council for Environmental Education on the evaluation and profiling of environmental education within the context of the National Curriculum.

For the last 8 years, I have been developing the primary school programme at WWF-UK, working closely with schools to develop innovative models for education for sustainable development and producing support materials for teachers. I also had the privilege to facilitate international workshops with teacher trainers and government representatives in Europe, Sri Lanka and Cameroon.

My career in environmental education has enabled me to combine my passion for the natural environment with my interests in people and other cultures. Having two young children, I feel that my work is worthwhile not only to help protect the world for them in the future but also to encourage in them positive attitudes towards the environment and towards different cultures and ways of life. It is gratifying to see my children develop a similar interest in the environment and the world!"

Tim Morton - Ecobus Manager, Royal Borough of Windsor and Maidenhead

"On leaving college with a Building and Surveying Diploma, I trained and worked with a surveying company as a Land and Building Surveyor, working for the construction industry. A life-changing experience then led me to re-evaluate what I was doing and I set up my own small business to see if I could do it. Although successful, I felt it was not right for me and I signed up to a Community Worker course run by PACT Community Projects. I subsequently found a placement as a volunteer with the Blackwater Valley Project and, before the end of the course, was employed as a Project Assistant and then Community Liaison Manager for the newly created Blackwater Valley Recreation and Countryside Management Service.

Part of my work involved working with local schools and I decided I should try my hand at teaching. I undertook a geography degree, followed by a PGCE as a mature student. The last part of the course included a day on Values and Development Education. I concluded that this was a highly undervalued area of education, and that this was where I wanted to develop my career. I subsequently applied for my current post, that of Environmental Awareness Officer with the Royal Borough of Windsor and Maidenhead. Since the main resource I manage is the Borough's 'Ecobus', my usual title is Ecobus Manager!

I have responsibility for managing every aspect of this unique resource, a mobile exhibition and information centre with a primary focus on education. However, in addition to schools and colleges, the service is extended to businesses, organisations and the public in general.

I see my main role as providing assistance and encouragement to schools in their delivery of Education for Sustainable Development (ESD) and, more recently, Citizenship. The schools do the preliminary hard work and then the Ecobus arrives to illustrate it. Alternatively, the Ecobus is used as a springboard, introducing the issues prior to the start of a scheme of work or project within the school. The role of schools is not just to equip young people for a future society, but also to shape that society. The future has to be sustainable. The bottom line is all about relationships: being aware of how the way we live our lives affects the lives that others are able to live.

What I like about the job is that I get to think a lot about the best way to communicate a wide range of different issues and then have fun doing it with an unusual resource. Although the impact in terms of numbers is inevitably limited, I know that I am able to make an important difference. This is especially encouraging when you know that you have contributed not only to improved academic performance but also to improved awareness and an ability to change things. I know that makes me very fortunate and I look at it as a serious responsibility. And then, of course, I also get to drive a BIG bus!

The main drawback is that the Ecobus is a massive resource and keeping it (and myself) running and up to date with the latest developments is a constant challenge. I know that I won't be able to keep going in this post indefinitely, but there is much more still to do and I am still having fun so I am not in a hurry to hand it on just yet!"

Margaret Feneley - Conservation Officer (with responsibility for publicity and communications), English Nature

"My first degree was a BA Hons in Combined Arts (Geography, French and German) at Leicester University. I then spent 3 years working for the British Schools Exploring Society, based at the Royal Geographical Society in London, organising science and adventure expeditions overseas for young people aged 16 to 20.

I left to travel for 8 months around Australia and south east Asia. On my return I looked for a post focusing on environment or development issues. I accepted the post of Policy Research Officer at the Council for Environmental Education, a national umbrella body co-ordinating, promoting and influencing environmental education policy and practice.

My role originally focused on informal education (youth work), promoting opportunities for young people to learn about environmental issues beyond the school curriculum. This was an exciting time for the movement with the rise of education for sustainable development (ESD). I subsequently took on responsibility for the area of biodiversity education, working particularly on the integration of education and awareness into UK biodiversity policy.

After ten years I wanted to focus more on the scientific/ecological aspects of biodiversity and studied part time for an MSc in Biodiversity & Conservation at Leeds University. I then took up my present post - Conservation Officer with an English Nature local team. Although primarily concerned with the conservation and management of designated sites, my previous experience means I am well placed to contribute to English Nature's commitment to linking people and wildlife. It also meant I was offered the publicity and communications role for the team. I find that having a national policy background brings an important context and overview to my work at a local level."

Jonathan Somper - Self-employed Environmental and Marketing Consultant

"When I graduated from Reading University with a Combined Social Science degree, I wanted to work as a researcher for wildlife documentaries. However, it soon became apparent that not having a biologically-based degree was a serious drawback and I was advised to go away and get a 'relevant skill'.

Hoping to learn more about marketing and business skills, I became involved with a series of enterprises (including the wholesale distribution of American wine and the opening of a French restaurant in Soho, which rapidly acquired cult status!). I then went to Kenya and Tanzania to realise a childhood dream. During this time I discussed job prospects with conservation experts and subsequently returned to take up the post of Marketing Manager for the Nature Conservancy Council, before it was reconstituted as English Nature.

Subsequently I relocated to the Cotswolds, providing marketing and management assistance to the International Centre for Conservation Education, a small charity providing environmental education resources and training for trainers and resource managers around the world. Following further management-based studies (MBA course at Gloucester University), I now offer marketing and management support to charitable groups in the environmental sector.

A number of my clients are organisations with an interest in environmental education, such as the Wildlife Trusts, the Council for Environmental Education, Groundwork and the Wildfowl and Wetlands Trust. Many of these organisations recognise the need to promote their education services and to evaluate the impact of their work. My experience of both marketing and working in the environmental education field qualifies me to do this."

Contacts

Association of National Park Authorities of England and Wales (ANPA)
c/o Ponsford House, Moretonhampstead, Devon TQ13 8NL
Tel: 01647 440245
www.anpa.gov.uk

Black Environment Network (BEN)
9 Llainwen Uchaf, Llanberis, Wales LL55 4LL
Tel: 01286 870715
www.ben-network.org.uk

Botanic Gardens Education Network (BGEN)
c/o Royal Botanic Gardens (Edinburgh), 20a Inverleith Row, Edinburgh EH3 5LR
Tel: 0131 248 2962

British Trust for Conservation Volunteers (BTCV)
36 St Mary's Street, Wallingford, Oxfordshire OX10 0EU
Tel: 01491 821600
www.btcv.org

Centre for Alternative Technology (CAT)
Machynlleth, Powys SY20 9AZ
Tel: 01654 703743
www.cat.org.uk

Centre for Research, Education and Training in Energy (CREATE)
Kenley House, 25 Bridgeman Terrace, Wigan WN1 1TD
Tel: 01942 322271
www.create.org.uk

Council for Environmental Education (CEE)
94 London Street, Reading RG1 4SJ
Tel: 01189 502550
www.cee.org.uk

Countryside Foundation for Education (CFE)
PO Box 8, Hebden Bridge HX7 5YJ
Tel: 01422 885566
www.countrysidefoundation.org.uk

Development Education Association (DEA)
29-31 Cowper Street, London EC2A 4AP
Tel: 020 7490 8108
www.dea.org.uk

English Heritage
English Heritage Education Service, 23 Saville Row, London W15 2ET
Tel: 020 7973 3442
www.english-heritage.org.uk

Environment Agency
Rio House, Waterside Drive, Aztec West, Almondsbury, Bristol BS32 4UD
Tel: 01454 624400
www.environment-agency.gov.uk

Farming and Countryside Education (FACE)
National Agricultural Centre, Stoneleigh Park, Warwickshire CV8 2LZ
Tel: 024 7653 5707
www.face-online.org.uk

Federation of City Farms and Community Gardens (FCFCG)
The Green House, Hereford Street, Bedminster, Bristol BS3 4NA
Tel: 0117 923 1800
www.farmgarden.org.uk

Field Studies Council (FSC)
Preston Montford, Montford Bridge, Shrewsbury SY4 1HW
Tel: 01743 850674
www.field-studies-council.org

Forest Education Initiative (FEI)
Great Eastern House, Tenison Road, Cambridge CB1 2DU
Tel: 01223 314546
www.foresteducation.org

Friends of the Earth (FOE)
26-28 Underwood Street, London N1 7JQ
Tel: 020 7490 1555
www.foe.co.uk

Global Action Plan
8 Fulwood Place, London WC1V 6HG
Tel: 020 7405 5633
www.globalactionplan.org.uk

Groundwork
85/87 Cornwall Street, Birmingham B3 3BY
Tel: 0121 216 8565
www.groundwork.org.uk

Learning Through Landscapes (LTL)
3rd Floor, Southside Offices, The Law Courts, Winchester SO23 9DL
Tel: 01962 846258
www.ltl.org.uk

Living Earth
4 Great James Street, London WC1N 3DA
Tel: 020 7242 3816
www.livingearth.org.uk

National Association for Environmental Education (NAEE)
Wolverhampton University, Walsall Campus, Gorway Road, Walsall, West Midlands WS1 3BD
Tel: 01922 631200
www.naee.co.uk

National Association of Field Studies Officers (NAFSO)
c/o Stibbington Centre for Environmental Education, Great North Road, Stibbington, Peterborough, Cambridgeshire PE8 6LP
Tel: 01780 782386
www.nafso.org.uk

National Association for Clean Air and Environmental Protection (NSCA)
44 Grand Parade, Brighton BN2 2QA
Tel: 01273 878770
www.nsca.org.uk

National Trust
26 Queen Anne's Gate, London SW1H 9AS
Tel: 020 7222 9251
www.nationaltrust.org.uk

Oxfam Development Education Programme
247 Banbury Road, Oxford OX2 7DZ
Tel: 01865 313 185
www.oxfam.org.uk/coolplanet/teachers/oxeduc.htm

Places for People
c/o ETP, 9 South Road, Brighton BN1 6SB
Tel: 01273 542660

Royal Society for the Protection of Birds (RSPB)
The Lodge, Sandy, Bedfordshire SG19 2DL
Tel: 01767 680551
www.rspb.org.uk

Scottish Natural Heritage (SNH)
12 Hope Terrace, Edinburgh EH12 9AS
Tel: 0131 446 2293
www.snh.org.uk

Sustrans
35 King Street, Bristol Bs! 4DZ
Tel: 0117 929 0888
www.sustrans.org.uk

Waste Watch
96 Tooley Street, London SE1 2JH
Tel: 020 7089 2100
www.wastewatch.org.uk

The Wildfowl and Wetlands Trust
Slimbridge, Gloucestershire GL2 7BT
Tel: 01453 890333
www.wwt.org.uk

The Wildlife Trusts
The Kiln, Waterside, Mather Road, Newark, Nottinghamshire NG24 1WT
Tel: 01636 677711
www.wildlifetrust.org.uk

The Woodcraft Folk
13 Ritherdon Road, London SW17 8QE
Tel: 020 8672 6031
www.woodcraft.org.uk

WWF-UK
Panda House, Weyside Park, Godalming, Surrey GU7 1XR
Tel: 01483 426449
www.wwf.org.uk

Websites

www.cee.org.uk - This is the website of the Council for Environmental Education (CEE). It is a link site for a large number of organisations with an interest in environmental education/ESD, which can be accessed directly through the CEE site.

www.wssd-education.org.uk - A website containing information about ESD in relation to the Johannesburg World Summit in August/September 2002.

www.nc.uk.net/esd - A website run by the Qualifications and Curriculum Authority (QCA) mainly relating to ESD in schools.

Publications

CEE Mail A termly publication produced by the Council for Environmental Education (CEE), aimed mainly at teachers but containing useful information on resources, organisations, events, competitions and awards. CEE also produces *CEE View* for its members, which contains information about recent developments in the field.

All the main organisations involved in environmental education/ESD produce regular *publications* of various kinds - these are listed on the CEE website (www.cee.org.uk) under the relevant organisations.

Job vacancies are normally advertised in the *Times Educational Supplement* and in the broadsheet newspapers, such as *The Guardian*.

References

Department of the Environment, Transport and the Regions (1998) *First Annual Report of the Sustainable Development Education Panel*

7. Nature Conservation & Biodiversity
Elaine Hayes, Sussex Wildlife Trust & Andrew Barker, Bullen Consultants Ltd

The Sector

This very broad sector encompasses a diverse range of careers across the whole of industry and beyond into the voluntary sector. Conservation in its broadest sense covers rural and urban landscapes, flora and fauna, recreation and education (usually termed interpretation), together with maintenance and enhancement of our natural environment.

Biodiversity embraces our efforts to protect what remains of the wildlife in the world. Much of the work focuses on identifying and recording species presence and abundance. Developing a robust understanding of the needs of individual species and how they interact is an integral part of the process. This can then be transferred into Biodiversity Action Plans (BAPs). These Plans were one of the outcomes of the United Nations Conference on Environment and Development (UNCED), commonly known as the 'Earth Summit', which was held in Rio de Janeiro in 1992. In addition to BAPs, plans are also generated for species and habitats. All of these have to be developed and then implemented, so there is much to do.

Sector Profile

Environmental conservation employs an estimated 56,000 people working for around 5,000 organisations. There are also many voluntary conservation jobs, and employers actively seek individuals who have undertaken voluntary work. The conservation sector employs a highly qualified workforce with up to 66% having higher education qualifications.

The number of jobs in the conservation sector is predicted to grow by approximately 4% per year, the increase being fuelled by increased interest in the environment amongst the population coupled with enhanced funding opportunities for conservation from the National Lottery and the European Union.

Typical Post Names

Ecologist, Biodiversity Officer, Conservation Officer, Reserves Officer, Landscape Officer, Ranger, Environmental Scientist, Ecological Records Officer.

Main Employers

- Government bodies e.g. Department for the Environment, Food and Rural Affairs (DEFRA), English Nature, Environment Agency, Countryside Agency
- Local and regional government
- Consultancies
- Charities e.g. Wildlife Trusts, RSPB, National Park Authorities
- Large utilities e.g. Water Companies
- Some large scale manufacturing businesses

Career Opportunities

Developing a career in this area is challenging. Ecological and conservation jobs are some of the most sought after posts and this is certainly not due to the high salaries they attract. Most people within the sector have undertaken some form of post-graduate qualification and have often responded to job vacancies advertised at well below their level of qualifications. A typical Wildlife Trust job for a Reserves Officer would attract in excess of 500 applicants for a post that offers a salary of £15,000 to £20,000.

Consultancies offer a diverse range of projects and therefore need a broad skill base. Identification skills are greatly sought after by consultancies and this is something which is rarely taught on undergraduate or postgraduate courses.

Public sector
There is a broad range of careers in this sector across the full range of organisations. Central, regional and local government all employ ecologists and/or conservationists to a senior level although the level of funding for these posts varies depending upon the perceived local priorities.

Within the public sector there are a wide range of posts from junior civil servants through to jobs at the most senior level. Competition is fierce with the majority of applicants being qualified to at least degree level. There are also roles at County and District level in local authorities, often embracing other areas such as landscape or parks.

Prospects for promotion can be limited as the posts are hard won in the first place. Individuals often need to move organisation in order to progress.

Private sector
Many large companies with land interests will employ their own ecologist/ conservationist but these can often be single jobs within an environmental portfolio department. This can be quite daunting to inexperienced ecologists and there may be a requirement for at least three years experience for posts in companies who employ only one ecologist. Knowledge of current issues and trends and a good working knowledge of current legislation and how it affects the business is normally essential for posts in manufacturing, utilities and development/construction businesses.

Due to the nature of such organisations, career opportunities for ecologists are rare and for conservationists almost non existent. Therefore a much more likely career path in the private sector is with a consultancy. There are many private consultancies ranging from small specialist ecological, land management and practical conservationist practices, to larger multi-disciplinary consultancies which have an ecology and nature conservation section as part of the larger business (which invariably started life as an engineering consultancy but cannot now survive without an environmental emphasis).

These consultancies are likely to employ staff with a range of experience and expertise. New graduate starters with little or no experience can expect salaries of £13,000 to £15,000. MSc graduates may start slightly higher, depending on the size and nature of the consultancy. Such businesses are less likely to have the rigid pay scales of the government bodies and salary reviews are generally undertaken on performance and inevitably profitability. Employers are usually looking for environmental science degrees or biological/geographical degrees, which have included elements of ecology/nature conservation and biodiversity. MSc graduates would normally have undertaken more specialist ecologically based courses.

Career prospects in the private sector are very much based on the performance of the individual within the team which in turn is based on the skills, enthusiasm and experience of the staff.

'Not for profit' sector
This sector accounts for a significant proportion of the jobs market in environmental conservation. Volunteers form a major part of the 'not for profit' workforce and as a result entry to this part of the sector often requires volunteering experience in addition to formal qualifications.

Work in the 'not for profit' sector continues to grow as a result of the increasing funding available from the National Lottery and also the European Union. Many of these jobs are contract posts and therefore job security can be uncertain.

Issues and Trends

Issues in conservation primarily concern retaining, restoring and enhancing habitats for the benefit of wildlife. On the face of it this would seem relatively straightforward but the pressures on land in the UK for development and transport infrastructure mean that much time is taken up with evaluating the best environmental option and endeavouring to quantify costs and benefits.

People's awareness of environmental issues has increased and continues to do so, fuelled by the work of NGOs and other pressure groups. Global warming is inevitably the focus of much attention as we strive to understand how this will affect biodiversity in the UK. Increases in flooding may result in loss of habitat but more effective use of natural floodplains also presents opportunities.

The Water Framework Directive now figures greatly in our deliberations, being possibly the most radical and extensive piece of water legislation ever. The landscape of our thinking will have to change in order to ensure sustainable holistic catchment management.

Since the Foot and Mouth epidemic much attention has focused on the state of the countryside that is under management by the farming community. Reform of the Common Agricultural Policy will afford further opportunities for jobs in an advisory capacity within farming communities. New 'broad and shallow' funding schemes should change the very landscape of farming away from high intensity production and down the route of sustainability. There is much to do in this area and the challenges ahead will present future generations of conservationists with complex, interesting and challenging issues.

The pressures on the environment from development are ever increasing and legislation is now in place to ensure that wherever possible development is designed and located to minimise impact on the environment. Nowadays most new developments will require an Environmental Impact Assessment, a significant part of which is the Ecology and Nature Conservation Section. Work in this area has increased significantly over the past decade and shows no signs of slowing down.

Personal Profiles

Phil Griffiths - Regional Conservation Officer, Environment Agency

"In 1986 I left school armed with 9 'O' Levels and three 'A' Levels in Chemistry, Biology and Mathematics/Statistics as well as a couple of months voluntary experience gained at my local Wildlife Trust Nature Reserve in North Wales.

I studied Ecology at the University of Lancaster from 1986 to 1989, where I obtained a Lower Second Class degree. Following further voluntary experience at Leighton Moss Nature Reserve in the summer I decided to enrol on an MSc course in Remote Sensing of the Environment and graduated in 1990.

I secured employment with the then National Rivers Authority in 1991 as a River Corridor Surveyor, a job which I did for a couple of years until I became Assistant Conservation and Recreation Officer in Sussex. A couple of years later I was promoted to Sussex Area Conservation Officer and in 1996 became Sussex Area Conservation Team Leader, helping ensure that the newly formed Environment Agency complied with its statutory conservation duties and relevant legislation.

I held this post until 2001 when I felt I needed to broaden my experience somewhat and took on a short internal secondment as the Regional External Funding Manager before returning to become Regional Conservation Officer in May 2001. In this role, I am responsible for the interpretation and influencing of national policy and legislation and ensuring consistent application across the region."

Nadine Russell - Biodiversity Records Officer, Sussex Biodiversity Record Centre

"I am the Biodiversity Records Officer at the Sussex Biodiversity Record Centre, a partnership project of local authorities, English Nature and non-governmental organisations (NGOs) that is housed at one of our partners, the Sussex Wildlife Trust. I came to work in conservation indirectly after graduating from university in Canada with a BA in Colonial History, which led me to teach English in Poland and Japan. I went on to gain an MSc in Conservation: Protected Landscape Management and Development.

After a year of volunteering at the Record Centre I had the skills base to apply for my current position. As Biodiversity Records Officer I am responsible for answering enquiries, managing a team of volunteers, maintaining and updating two databases and a Geographical Information System or mapping programme. I am also the webmaster for the Record Centre."

Elaine Hayes - Director, Sussex Wildlife Trust

"I graduated from London University with a degree in Animal Physiology but few work prospects. I decided to do an MSc in Aquatic Resource Management that included an industrial placement as part of the qualification. I spent three months with Severn Trent Water who then offered me a job. I stayed with Severn Trent for six years working my way through the organisation and completing two BTEC courses, one in sewage treatment, the second in operational management. During that time I also became a full member of CIWEM.

I decided that I needed experience in industry and left to help establish an environmental consultancy that specialised in toxicity and treatability issues. The business was taken over and I became Business Manager for WRc-NSF, which is part of the WRc Group (one of the large water-based consultancies in the UK). I felt my career had taken a wrong turn as I was remote from environmental matters that are so important to me. I saw the move to the Wildlife Trust as a way of contributing more effectively.

I have been at the Sussex Wildlife Trust for eight months and I love the job. It is varied and challenging; the work the Trust does is fantastic and I really feel that I am putting something back and making an important contribution to nature conservation in the UK."

Richard Wardle - Graduate Environmental Scientist, Bullen Consultants Ltd

"I left school in 1992 with eight GCSEs and three 'A' Levels in Chemistry, Biology and Geography. I knew that a career in the environment was for me, but was unsure at this stage exactly which aspect suited me best.

I took a year out before university, half of which was spent with my local countryside service, before enrolling at Sheffield University on their Natural Environmental Science degree. An aptitude and preference for the ecological aspects of the degree saw me change course at the end of my first year to Plant Science, in which I obtained an Upper Second Class degree.

The following three years were spent in temporary employment, voluntary work and travelling in South America during which time I was able to plan the direction in which my career should go. I decided that there were more opportunities available in contaminated land assessment and remediation, despite the fact that I was most interested in ecology. I enrolled on the Environmental Science MSc course at Aberdeen University, where I specialised in soil science, assessment and remediation of contaminated land. I passed with distinction, but for the following six months was unable to find employment in this field.

An opportunity came up at Bullen Consultants that enabled me to return to the ecological side of environmental science. I secured the job and have been on their Natural Environment team for just over a year, during which time I have undertaken surveys of a wide variety of flora and fauna for many different projects. It is my role to assess the ecological sensitivity of any location that is scheduled for development and to provide site-specific remedial measures to preserve or enhance its ecological status."

Andrew Barker - Divisional Manager, Bullen Consultants Ltd

"I graduated from Kingston University in 1989 with a degree in Geography but with a significant proportion of my final year covering ecological/nature conservation modules. I knew I wanted to work in ecology and nature conservation but had no experience other than my degree. Competition was fierce at the time and it took me several months to find a job. My first post was as Ecological Officer in a local government Ecology Unit in West Yorkshire and my first project was large scale habitat survey of Calderdale District in West Yorkshire. This provided me with invaluable experience of identifying habitats and species as well as keeping me fit walking ten miles or so every day through the South Pennines. As well as ecological project work I was also involved in surveying sites of nature conservation importance, assessing the ecological implications of planning applications and advising the authorities on ecological issues for Local Development Plans.

I stayed with the Local Authority for seven years eventually managing the unit, but after this time felt my chances of further promotion were limited particularly if I wanted to stay in ecology and therefore moved to the private sector. I was approached by Bullens in 1998 to manage and expand the ecological and wider environmental section which includes a team of ecologists, archaeologists and landscape architects.

My role now is very much project management and management of staff, and whilst I miss the field surveying to a certain extent (and take every opportunity to go out on surveys particularly when the weather is decent), I am very happy in my job."

Contacts

ADAS
Oxford Spires Business Park, Kidlington, Oxon, OX5 1NZ
Tel: 01345 660085
www.adas.co.uk

British Trust for Ornithology
The Nunnery, Thetford, Norfolk, IP24 2PU
Tel: 01842 750050
www.bto.org

British Waterways
Willow Grange, Church Road, Watford, Herts, WD1 3QA
Tel: 01923 226422
www.britishwaterways.co.uk

Centre for Ecology and Hydrology
Monks Wood, Abbotts Ripton, Huntingdon, Cambridgeshire, PE28 2LS
Tel: 01487 772400
www.ceh.ac.uk

Countryside Council for Wales
Maes Ffynnon, Fford Penrhos, Bangor, LL57 2DN
Tel: 01248 385500
www.ccw.gov.uk

Council for the Protection of Rural England
Warwick House, 25 Buckingham Palace Road, London, SW1 W0
Tel: 020 7976 6433
www.cpre.org.uk

Countryside Agency
John Dower House, Crescent Place, Cheltenham, Gloucestershire, GL50 3RA
Tel: 01242 521381
www.countryside.gov.uk

Department for Environment, Food and Rural Affairs (DEFRA)
Nobel House, 17 Smith Square, London, SW1P 3JR
Tel: 020 7238 6000
www.defra.gov.uk

English Nature
Northminster House, Peterborough, PE1 1UA
Tel: 01733 455000
www.english-nature.org.uk

Enviroment Agency
Rio House, Waterside Drive, Aztec West, Almondsbury, Bristol, BS32 4UD
Tel: 01454 624400
www.environment-agency.gov.uk

Forestry Commission
231 Corstorphine Road, Edinburgh, EH12 7AT
Tel: 0131 334 0303
www.forestry.gov.uk

Farming and Wildlife Advisory Group
The National Agriculture Centre, Stoneleigh, Kenilworth, CV8 2RX
Tel: 02476 696 699
www.fwag.org.uk

Joint Nature Conservation Committee
Monkstone House, City Road, Peterborough, PE1 1JY
Tel: 01733 866900
www.jncc.gov.uk

Lantra Trust
Lantra House, National Agricultural Centre, Kenilworth, Warwickshire, CV8 2LG
Tel: 024 7669 6996
www.lantra.co.uk

Local Government Association
Local Government House, Smith Square, London, SW1P 3HZ
Tel: 020 7664 3000
www.lga.gov.uk

Royal Society for Nature Conservation
The Green, Nettleham, Lincolnshire, LN2 2NR
Tel: 01636 677711
www.rsnc.org.uk

Royal Society for the Protection of Birds
The Lodge, Sandy, Bedfordshire, SG19 2DL
Tel: 01767 680551
www.rspb.org.uk

Scottish Environmental Protection Agency
Erskine Court, The Castle Business Park, Stirling, FK9 4TR
Tel: 01786 457 700
www.sepa.org.uk

Scottish Natural Heritage
12 Hope Terrace, Edinburgh, EH9 2AS
Tel: 0131 447 4784
www.snh.org.uk

Institutions

British Ecological Society
26 Blades Court, Putney, London, SW15 2NU
Tel: 020 8871 9797
www.britishecologicalsociety.org

Institute of Biology
20-22 Queensbury Place, London, SW7 2DZ
Tel: 0207 7581 8333
www.iob.org

Institute of Ecology and Environmental Management
36 Kingfisher Court, Hambridge Road, Newbury, Berkshire, RG14 5SJ
Tel: 01635 37715
www.ieem.co.uk

Institute of Environmental Management and Assessment
St Nicholas House, 70 Newport, Lincoln, LN1 3DP
Tel: 01522 540069
www.iema.net

Journals and Magazines

Some of the most useful journals and magazines which advertise courses and jobs are:

British Wildlife
ENDS (Environmental Data Services)
In Practice
New Scientist
The Biologist
The Environment Post
The Environmentalist
The Guardian newspaper (on Wednesdays)
Water and Environment Manager

Internet Resources

There are numerous websites that cover conservation and biodiversity. We would recommend the following:

Countryside Jobs Service
www.countryside-jobs.com

Department for Environment, Food and Rural Affairs (see Contacts section)

Edie
www.edie.net

ENDS
www.ends.com

Environment Agency (see Contacts section)

Growing Careers
www.growing-careers.com

Naturenet
www.naturenet.net

8. Landscape

Jenifer White, English Heritage

We would like to thank The Landscape Institute for kindly giving us permission to use material from their website and careers leaflets in this chapter.

The Sector

The landscape sector embraces many specialists, such as landscape architects, horticulturalists, gardeners and ecologists. Careers in the sector range from work with specific landscape types or land-uses (such as gardens, parks, golf courses and wildlife sites) to strategic planning and policy; with contrasts like urban regeneration and countryside conservation, new design and heritage landscapes, and public, private and voluntary organisations. The landscape sector works closely with other professions such as planning, architecture and engineering.

Sector Profile

As this sector is diverse, there are no overall employment figures. The Landscape Institute, a professional body for landscape practitioners, has 4,500 members of whom half work in the public sector and half work in private practice, commerce and industry.

For example, Groundwork, a leading environmental regeneration charity with local Trusts, employs 1,500 people. The Countryside Council for Wales, the Government's statutory adviser on sustaining natural beauty, wildlife, and access to the countryside in Wales, employs 661 staff. English Heritage, a Government agency, has a team of 5 landscape architects, 6 landscape managers, 2 horticulturists, 9 head gardeners and garden curators (plus gardeners), 1 landscape planner and 2.75 landscape history specialists!

The number of landscape courses offered reflects the growth in this sector over the last 25 years, although some landscape work may fluctuate with economic downturns.

Typical Post Names

Landscape Architect, Landscape Manager, Landscape Planner, Landscape Consultant, Landscape Designer, Landscape Scientist, Conservation Officer, Horticulturist, Gardener.

Main Employers

Local authorities, public sector organisations (e.g. the Countryside Agency), landscape design and management businesses, and non-government organisations (e.g. Groundwork).

Career Opportunities

Many of those employed in the sector are *landscape architects*. Landscape architecture is concerned with the long-term care of landscapes, habitat creation and the reclamation of derelict land, urban regeneration and planning landscapes at a strategic level. Landscape architects work on all types of external space - large or small, urban or rural - and with 'hard' or 'soft' materials. The Landscape Institute describes the work of the different disciplines of landscape architecture as follows:

Landscape designers are involved in the planning and design of all types of outdoor spaces. They use design techniques based on their knowledge of the functional and aesthetic characteristics of landscape materials and of the organisation of the landscape elements, external places and activities. Their work ranges from large-scale landscape planning to the preparation of schemes for the short and long-term development of individual sites. It also includes the preparation of detailed designs, specifications, contract drawings, and the supervision of contracts. In urban areas, their work is largely concerned with public spaces, built developments and urban regeneration. In rural areas, the emphasis is on tourist landscapes, agriculture, forestry, land reclamation and the extraction industry.

Landscape managers specialise in the long-term care, conservation, enhancement and development of new and existing landscapes. Their expertise lies in the careful management and maintenance of hard and soft landscapes, based on established principles of land use patterns, construction, horticulture and ecology. The landscape manager will also have a thorough knowledge of budgetary control procedures, property and resource management, and of letting and administrating contracts. Landscape managers are normally educated in horticulture, forestry, agriculture or natural sciences and have further training in land management or related disciplines.

Landscape scientists investigate and explore the geology, wildlife and natural features that make up the landscape. They have scientific training in subjects such as soil science, ecology, biology, hydrology, geomorphology, botany, or related disciplines, and relate their environmental training, research and experience to the solution of practical landscape problems, providing both traditional and innovative input to landscape design, planning and management work. Evaluation of the significance, effects and possible amelioration of planning proposals, along with creating new habitats and environments in association with mineral workings, forestry, and agriculture, are significant roles of the landscape scientist.

Specialisation and diversity increasingly characterise the profession of landscape architecture. Landscape planners, for example, are concerned with the location, scenic, ecological and recreational aspects of urban, rural and coastal land use. They take an overview, planning the evolution of the built and natural landscape in all dimensions. Exciting opportunities also exist in the growing areas of urban design, environmental art, landscape archaeology and private estate and garden design.

Most new entrants to the landscape sector have gained a degree in landscape architecture, which can be studied either full or part-time at undergraduate or postgraduate level, or have undertaken training such as a gardeners apprenticeship scheme. The Landscape Institute website includes a list of undergraduate, graduate and landscape management courses which lead to graduate membership of the Institute. The web site for Lantra, the Sector Skills Council for the environment and land-based sector, includes advice on careers and modern apprenticeships. Please refer to the Contacts section at the end of the chapter for details of these websites.

Organisations such as English Heritage, the National Council for the Conservation of Plants and Gardens (NCCPG) and some private sector practices offer training positions on an annual basis for year-out students. Please refer to Chapter 4 on Student Placements for further information.

Practical site management and landscape contract implementation experience is essential to career development. Individuals can often enhance their employment prospects by gaining experience through working as a volunteer. Good oral and written communication skills and organisational skills are also needed. Skills like Computer Aided Design (CAD) and knowledge of other IT applications and their uses in landscape and project management are useful. Some jobs such as professional gardeners are physically demanding, and others involve travelling to sites so may require a driving licence.

Many landscape professionals start out in the public sector, working for local authorities or non-government organisations like Groundwork, then move on to other employers or run their own businesses when they have gained experience.

Salaries within the landscape sector vary considerably, with Head Gardeners earning from £14,000 to £20,000 and experienced Landscape Architects and Landscape Managers being paid between £25,000 and £40,000. Salaries in the public and private sectors are broadly similar. Higher salaries can be achieved by successful individuals, business entrepreneurs or those who take on broader corporate management roles and responsibilities.

Issues and Trends

Urban regeneration is one of the Government's priorities and the landscape professions have a key role to play in this through planning, design and maintenance. At the time of writing, the Government's Urban Green Spaces Taskforce had recommended that a new agency should be set up to champion and co-ordinate green spaces. The Heritage Lottery Fund Urban Parks Initiative is the catalyst for many public park restoration schemes and other Lottery funds have also helped fund green space improvements. The Urban Green Spaces Taskforce's Working Group 6 report on *Resources* (Department for Transport, Local Government and the Regions, May 2002) includes a chapter on training and development issues for qualified staff. This can be found on the internet at: www.urban.odpm.gov.uk/index.htm.

Farming and the rural economy are undergoing great changes with more agriculture and forestry funding being channelled to bring about wildlife, landscape and public access gains. Rural businesses have had to adapt and diversify. Previous agricultural policy has led to a loss of traditional landscape management and rural craft skills. It would be desirable to provide greater support for land owners and managers in applying for grants, however current economics mean that such job opportunities remain limited.

Personal Profiles

Liz Lake - Head of Practice, Liz Lake Associates

"As a child, I always wanted to be the person who designated the scenic routes and panoramic views on the Michelin road maps but it was not until a careers advisor suggested Landscape Architecture that I realized it was a proper job. After four years studying Landscape Architecture at Manchester Polytechnic, I worked for three years in landscape practices in London on quarries, power stations, vehicle test tracks, housing and cemeteries. I then had two years at the Greater London Council Parks Department, a formative experience but one that directed me back to private practice.

For six years, I worked at Travers Morgan Planning. Among a range of engineering projects, I was fortunate in working on the A55 North Wales Coast Road with a very creative, multi disciplinary team of architects, engineers, planners and ecologists. In 1985, I left to combine my own practice with a young family. Both have grown.

Liz Lake Associates is based in Stansted, Essex with fourteen staff and now it is my turn to be setting up creative teams. Projects range from large scale landscape planning and development to smaller scale proposals in both the public and private sectors. My role now, as head of the practice, is to ensure that our work is technically proficient and answers the client's brief. I enjoy the business of running a practice but most of all I relish the challenge of the projects we have in the practice. Helping a client to solve a technically difficult problem, with a creative solution that is good for the landscape, is very rewarding. However, I am still waiting for the call from Michelin."

Sara Turton - Director, Livingston Eyre Associates

"I consider myself very, very lucky to be working as a Landscape Architect. Looking back, I could so easily have left school and headed off to University to study Maths or Biology or some other pure science. It seemed so tempting to go on to study a subject I already knew I was good at... but to what end? Inspired by my mother who was an Art teacher and my father who was a Structural Engineer, I chanced upon the description of 'Landscape Architect' leafing through the credits of Concrete Quarterly. Beautiful photographs of outdoor spaces crafted from magical blends of granite, steel, glass and concrete, enhanced and animated by the intense green light and shadow of foliage. Landscapes as backdrops and foregrounds for the built environment - yet at the same time, spaces for people to spend time outside those buildings, going in, coming out and everything in between.

After making a start at Sheffield University, knowing that there was a long way to go (7 years!), and needing some career reassurance, I started working in the holidays for a firm of Architects and Landscape Architects in the North West ... and I have never looked back! Fifteen years later I am in London working alongside some famous names and fabulous characters in the world of Architecture and watching some truly beautiful things being built, both in London and across the country. When I think of how close I came to spending my whole working life in a lab coat! Instead I find myself driving through towns thinking...
Those are my trees, aren't they looking fantastic now they've grown ...?
  ...Now which variety did we choose in the end ...?
    ...That leaf outline looks really good silhouetted against the glazing...
      ...It's great to see the space so full of people...
        ...I wonder if you can still get those gorgeous steel benches...?
          ...They would go really well on that new project in Manchester ...

Perhaps life in a lab coat would have been less complicated...!"

Contacts

The professional bodies' websites often include careers advice and information on qualifications and job opportunities. They can also provide lists of registered individuals and practices. Their journals and magazines often include features on individual members which illustrate potential career paths, types of work and employers. Relevant Government organisations advertise job vacancies on their websites, as do many other organisations (see below for details). Student posts are often advertised directly by colleges and universities, as well as in the publications listed below.

Most landscape sector jobs are advertised in the following publications:
· the Wednesday issue of the Guardian newspaper (www.guardian.co.uk)
· professional journals such as Landscape Design (www.landscape.co.uk)
· magazines and broadsheets such as Horticulture Week (www.hortweek.com), Landlines (www.landscape.co.uk), Regeneration and Renewal and The Environment Post.

Government organisations employing landscape specialists

Cadw
Cathays Parks, Cardiff, CF10 3NQ
Tel: 029 2050 0200
www.cadw.wales.gov.uk

Countryside Agency
John Dower House, Crescent Place, Cheltenham, Gloucestershire, GL50 3RA
Tel: 01242 521381
www.countryside.gov.uk

Countryside Council for Wales
Maes y Ffynnon, Ffordd Penrhos, Bangor, Gwynedd, LL57 2DN
Tel: 01248 385500
E-mail: enquiries@ccw.gov.uk
www.ccw.gov.uk

English Heritage
23 Savile Row, London, W1S 2ET
Tel: 020 7973 3000
www.english-heritage.org.uk

English Nature
Northminster House, Peterborough, PE1 1UA
Tel: 01733 455000
www.english-nature.org.uk

Environment Agency
Rio House, Waterside Drive, Aztec, West, Almondsbury, Bristol, BS32 4UD
Tel: 0845 9333111
www.environment-agency.gov.uk

Historic Scotland
Longmore House, Salisbury Place, Edinburgh, EH9 1SH
Tel: 0131 668 8600
www.historic-scotland.gov.uk

Scottish Natural Heritage
12 Hope Terrace, Edinburgh, EH9 2AS
Tel: 0131 447 4784
www.snh.org.uk

Sport England
116 Upper Woburn Place, London, WC1H 0QP
Tel: 0845 764 9649
www.sportengland.org

Organisations representing the landscape professions

AONB staff forum and The Association for AONBs (Areas of Outstanding Natural Beauty)
The Old Police Station, Cotswold Heritage Centre, Northleach, Gloucestershire, GL54 3JH
www.aonb.org.uk/staff/

British Association of Landscape Industries (BALI)
Landscape House, Stoneleigh Park, National Agricultural Centre, Warwickshire , CV8 2LG
Tel: 02476 690333
E-mail: membership@bali.org.uk
www.bali.org.uk

Countryside Management Association
Administration and General Enquiries, Writtle College, Lordship Road, Writtle, Chelmsford, Essex, CM1 3RR
Tel: 01245 424263
www.countrysidemanagement.org.uk

Institute of Environmental Management and Assessment (IEMA)
St Nicholas House, 70 Newport, Lincoln, LN1 3DP
Tel: 01522 540069
www.iema.net

Institute of Groundsmanship
19-23 Church Street, The Agora, Wolverton, Milton Keynes, Buckinghamshire, MK12 5LG
Tel: 01908 312511
E-mail:iog@iog.org
www.iog.org

Institute of Horticulture
14/15 Belgrave Square, London, SW1X 8PS
Tel/Fax: 020 7245 6943
E-mail: ioh@horticulture.org.uk
www.horticulture.org.uk

Institute of Leisure and Amenity Managers (ILAM)
ILAM House, Lower Basildon, Reading, RG8 9NE
Tel: 01491 874800
www.ilam.co.uk

The Landscape Institute
6-8 Barnard Mews, London, SW11 1QU
Tel: 020 7350 5200
E-mail: mail@l-i.org.uk
www.l-i.org.uk

Lantra Trust
Lantra House, National Agricultural Centre, Kenilworth, Warwickshire, CV8 2LG
Tel: 024 7669 6996
www.lantra.co.uk

Professional Gardeners Guild
Secretary, 2 Staff Quarters, Osborne House Estate, East Cowes, Isle of Wight,
PO32 6JZ
Tel: 01983 299747
www.pgg.org.uk

Royal Horticultural Society
Administrative Offices, Lindley Library and Exhibition Halls, 80 Vincent Square,
London, SW1P 2PE
Tel: 020 7834 4333
E-mail: info@rhs.org.uk
www.rhs.org.uk

Royal Institution of Chartered Surveyors (RICS)
RICS Contact Centre, Surveyor Court, Westwood Way, Coventry, CV4 8JE
Tel: 0870 333 1600
E-mail: contactrics@rics.org.uk
www.rics.org.uk

Society of Garden Designers
The Administrator, Park Farm Estates, Northmoor, Witney, Oxfordshire, OX29
5AZ
Tel: 01865 301523
E-mail: soc.gardendesign@btclick.com
www.society-of-garden-designers.co.uk

Urban Parks Forum
Caversham Court, Church Road, Caversham, Berkshire, RG4 7AD
Tel: 0118 946 9060
www.urbanparksforum.co.uk

**Non-government organisations employing landscape specialists or offering
volunteer opportunities to develop landscape skills**

Association of Garden Trusts
70 Cowcross Street, London, EC1M 6BP
Tel: 020 7251 2610
www.gardentrusts.co.uk

British Trust for Conservation Volunteers (BTCV)
36 St Mary's Street, Wallingford, Oxfordshire, OX10 0EU
Tel: 01491 821600
E-mail: information@btcv.org.uk
www.btcv.org.uk

Council for National Parks
246 Lavender Hill, London, SW11 1LJ
Tel: 020 7924 4077
E-mail: info@cnp.org.uk
www.cnp.org.uk

Council for the Protection of Rural England (CPRE)
Warwick House, 25 Buckingham Palace Road, London, SW1W 0PP
Tel: 020 7976 6433
E-mail: info@cpre.org.uk
www.cpre.org.uk

Garden History Society
70 Cowcross Street, London, EC1M 6BP
Tel: 020 7608 2409
www.gardenhistorysociety.org.uk

Growing Careers
www.growing-careers.com

Historic Houses Association
2 Chester Street, London SW1X 7BB
Tel: 020 7259 5688
E-mail: info@hha.org.uk
www.hha.org.uk

Groundwork UK
85-87 Cornwall Street, Birmingham, B3 3BY
Tel: 0121 236 8565
www.groundwork.org.uk

National Council for the Conservation of Plants and Gardens (NCCPG)
The Stable Courtyard, RHS Gardens, Wisley, Woking, Surrey, GU23 6QP
Tel: 01483 211465
E-mail: collections@nccpg.org.uk
www.nccpg.org.uk

The National Trust
36 Queen Anne's Gate, London, SW1H 9AS
Tel: 020 7222 9251
E-mail: enquiries@nationaltrust.org.uk
www.nationaltrust.org.uk

The National Trust for Scotland
Wemyss House, 28 Charlotte Square, Edinburgh, EH2 4ET
Tel: 0131 243 9300
E-mail: information@nts.org.uk
www.nts.org.uk

The Wildlife Trusts
The Kiln, Waterside, Mather Road, Newark , Nottinghamshire, NG24 1WT
Tel: 01636 677711
E-mail: info@wildlife-trusts.cix.co.uk
www.wildlifetrusts.org

9. Agriculture & Soil Science

Alison Holdsworth, Reading Agricultural Consultants Ltd, Simon Jones, Harper Adams University College, and Dr Stephen Nortcliff, University of Reading

The Sector

Agriculture occupies 85% of the land area of the UK and consequently impacts on the environment through many media. There is always a need to measure, analyse and control these impacts, whilst creating more sustainable farming methods which enhance food production and conserve flora and fauna.

Soil science is the study and investigation of the nature and behaviour of soils and soil management. Soils are important in agricultural production as the medium for plant growth, but also in the broader environmental context as the interface between the atmosphere and the underlying weathered and un-weathered geological materials and subsurface water stores. Soils play an exceptionally important role in buffering the effects of both natural phenomena (e.g. precipitation) and human activity (e.g. cultivation of crops or the spillage of a potential contaminant). The ability of soil to buffer these influences is a key component in helping to maintain our sustainable use of soil.

Sector Profile

It is difficult to estimate the numbers of those currently following environmental careers in either agriculture or soil science, as there is a great deal of overlap with other sectors. However, the sector is not a high employer, and there are fewer jobs in soil science than in agriculture.

Typical Post Names

Consultant, Soil Scientist, Environmental Protection Officer, Countryside Stewardship Officer, Water Quality Officer, Farm Waste Management Advisor, Conservation Officer

Main Employers

- Environment Agency
- Scottish Environment Protection Agency (SEPA)
- ADAS
- National Farmers Union (NFU)
- Department for Environment, Food and Rural Affairs (DEFRA)
- Farming and Wildlife Advisory Group (FWAG)
- National Trust
- Local Authorities
- The Game Conservancy Trust
- Wildlife Trusts
- English Nature
- Environmental consultancies

Career Opportunities

Agriculture: A good working knowledge of agriculture and a science-based qualification is needed (BSc/HND in Environmental Science, Geography,

Environmental Protection, Countryside Management, Biology etc). Conservation experience is also greatly beneficial. The balance between fieldwork and office-based work can vary considerably. Jobs are available in most areas and are not restricted to rural areas.

Soil Science: Specific opportunities for soil scientists are limited but knowledge of the nature and functioning of soils and soil materials is a major advantage in the understanding and management of broader environmental systems. The most relevant degrees include BSc Soil Science, BSc Environmental Science with a strong science component, BSc Geology or BSc Geography with a strong science component.

Soil scientists are a small group of scientists, but their employers are tremendously diverse. In the past there were substantial employment opportunities with national soil surveys and agricultural research and advisory bodies, but with the major changes in government funding these opportunities are now much more restricted. Now the major opportunities for soil scientists are with environmental consultancy companies. These companies are wide ranging in their spheres of interest and operation. They include traditional agricultural consultants, through those involved in waste management including composting, to companies involved with soil clean-up following contamination incidents or the restoration of brownfield sites to more productive use. There is increasing recognition that these areas of activity require an understanding of the nature and patterns of soil in the environment.

Typical starting salaries range from £9,000 to £16,000, while typical salaries at age 40 are between £16,000 and £28,000. Salaries may be lower in voluntary organisations.

Issues and Trends

In agriculture, *agri-environment schemes* form part of the England Rural Development Programme, which initially runs from 2000 to 2006. The schemes provide grants to conserve and improve the environment on a farm, and encourage sustainable management of uplands. They include hedge planting and laying, restoration of ponds and wet areas and the creation of species rich meadows. Additionally, these schemes aim to create more diverse agricultural jobs in the countryside.

At the time of writing, the Department for Environment, Food and Rural Affairs (DEFRA) had recently published a consultation paper *Sustainable Food and Farming: Working Together* (DEFRA, 2002), which aims to address the environmental impacts that farming can have on the landscape by considering options for controlling diffuse pollution of water from agriculture, including economic instruments, and the roles of agri-environment schemes and regulation.

For many years the study of soils has been the 'Cinderella' of the environmental sciences, with relatively little focus in terms of funding or research activity. In the last decade this has changed and soils are increasingly recognised as a potentially key component in many environmental systems. This increased awareness of the importance of soils was first highlighted by the publication, in 1996, of the 19th Report of the Royal Commission on Environmental Pollution entitled *The Sustainable Use of Soil*. This heralded a change in the 'visibility' of soil, and since this publication there has been an increased awareness of the potential importance of soils among national and European Ministries and Agencies.

The publication of *The Draft Soil Strategy for England* by DEFRA in 2001 is part of this increased awareness, highlighting the need to conserve soil, where possible maintain or improve its quality, and establish means of monitoring the nature of changes in soils and soil quality. In addition to this initiative at national level, the European Commission (EC) Directorate-General Environment produced *The Soil Protection Communication* in October 2001, which has many similarities to England's Soil Strategy. This EC document has been the subject of revision following extensive consultation and was recently considered at ministerial level. These initiatives emphasise an increasing recognition amongst practitioners and policy makers of the importance of soils within environmental systems, both natural and human-influenced.

Personal Profiles

Steve Fordham - Director, Reading Agricultural Consultants Ltd

"I graduated with a BSc in Geology, followed by a post-graduate Diploma in Soil Science. These studies taught me the importance of observation, reasoning from evidence, and the need to recognise where interpretation stops and speculation begins.

There followed 18 years describing, classifying and mapping soils with the Soil Survey of England and Wales. This practical experience, alas now effectively unavailable, provided me with the essential 'knowledge' of how soils work and how and why they vary from place to place - in short, giving me the beginnings of the ability to read the landscape. Without such experience, including the discipline to continue learning, I consider that one is ill-equipped to meet the many and varied challenges of consultancy work.

I joined a very small consultancy group as a soils specialist, rising to the position of Director. Although the group has grown substantially over the last 17 years, I have largely managed to maintain that position and its responsibilities. The group is multi-disciplinary and most members are self-employed - a challenge in itself. Work entails independent work and teamwork - as appropriate to particular projects. Peer-review of work is fierce and can, on occasions, be traumatic!

The company was fortunate to be involved with the environmental baseline studies and consequent mitigation measures in the construction of the Channel Tunnel, which was probably the first major construction project where a formal Environmental Impact Assessment was carried out. Mitigation of environmental impacts for habitat transfer and creation - amongst others - were planned in detail, supervised and implemented successfully. Understanding soil characteristics is fundamental to replicating the necessary conditions for a particular habitat to thrive. This experience has been built on and applied widely to other projects involving land disturbance, from small-scale excavation of minerals to large-scale restoration. The most recent application was the Channel Tunnel Rail Link, with habitat transfer and restoration of disturbed ground to agriculture both featuring strongly."

Dr Diane Mitchell - Environment Management Adviser, National Farmers' Union

"I studied Higher Level Biology, Chemistry, English, Mathematics (which proved to be very useful in the longer-term) and French. Following this I graduated with a degree in Soil Science from Aberdeen University. This provided a good grounding in all aspects of soil science including soil chemistry, soil physics, soil biology and fertility but also in areas such as water and nutrient supply to plants and land use and management. The balance of theoretical and practical hands-on aspects of the course and agronomic and environmental subject areas provided a very useful fundamental understanding of the science of soils.

After completing my degree, I studied for a PhD at the Macaulay Land Use Research Institute and Aberdeen University. I researched the impacts of the application of sewage sludge on nitrogen and phosphorus cycling in a mature forest stand. After leaving Aberdeen I worked at Cambridge University Farm as a potato agronomy research assistant for just over 2 years. This provided valuable practical experience in setting up and running field trials.

I now work for the National Farmers' Union as an Environment Management Adviser within the Environment and Rural Affairs Department. This covers helping to develop and deliver policies that affect farmers and growers in areas such as soil, waste issues, environmental liability and Integrated Pollution Prevention and Control (IPPC). My science, research and technical backgrounds have been very beneficial experience, and have helped to complement the policy work."

Contacts

Websites

ADAS
www.adas.co.uk/NewIndex/index.htm

British Geological Society
www.bgs.ac.uk

British Institute of Agricultural Consultants
www.biac.co.uk

British Trust for Conservation Volunteers (BTCV)
www.btcv.org.uk

Centre for Ecology and Hydrology
www.ceh-nerc.ac.uk

Countryside Agency
www.countryside.gov.uk

Department for Environment, Food & Rural Affairs (DEFRA)
www.defra.gov.uk

English Nature
www.english-nature.org.uk

Environment Agency
www.environment-agency.gov.uk

ENDS Report
www.endsreport.com

Farming & Wildlife Advisory Group
www.fwag.org.uk

Field Studies Council
www.field-studies-council.org

GeoData Institute (GIS)
www.geodata.soton.ac.uk

Growing Careers
www.growing-careers.com

Horticulture Research International
www.hri.ac.uk

Institute of Arable Crops Research
www.res.bbsrc.ac.uk

Institute of Freshwater Ecology
www.ife.ac.uk

Institute of Grassland Research
www.iger.bbsrc.ac.uk

Institute of Virology and Environmental Microbiology
www.nerc-oxford.ac.uk/ivem

John Innes Centre
www.jic.bbsrc.ac.uk

Lantra
www.lantra.co.uk/lantra/nto/welcome.htm

National Soil Resources Institute
www.silsoe.cranfield.ac.uk/nsri

National Trust
www.nationaltrust.org.uk

Royal Society for the Protection of Birds
www.rspb.org.uk

Scottish Natural Heritage
www.snh.org.uk

Silsoe Research Institute
www.sri.bbsrc.ac.uk

The Environment Council
www.greenchannel.com/tec

Wildlife Trusts
www.wildlifetrust.org.uk

Employment

Countryside Jobs Service
www.countryside-jobs.com

Jobs.ac.uk - www.jobs.ac.uk

National Grid Placement Scheme
Public Relations, National Grid House, Kirby Corner Road, Coventry CV4 8JY

National Soil Resources Institute
www.silsoe.cranfield.ac.uk/nsri

Net Temps
www.net-temps.com

Journals

Applied Soil Ecology
Biodegradation
Biology and Fertility of Soils
Environmental International
Environmental Pollution
European Journal of Soil Science
Journal of Agronomy and Crop Science
Journal of Agricultural Science
Journal of Science of Food and Agriculture
Journal of Soil Contamination
Journal of Soil and Water Conservation
Land Degradation and Development
Journal of Environmental Quality
Nature
New Scientist
Plant and Soil
Science of Soils
Soil and Tillage Research
Soil Science
Soil Science and Plant Nutrition
Soil Use and Management

Other Publications

The Guardian (on Wednesdays)
Farmers Weekly
The Grower
The Environment Post
Countryside Jobs Service (www.countryside-jobs.com)
BBC Wildlife magazine
Local Authority vacancy bulletins
ENDS Directory of Environmental Consultants
ENDS Report

References

Department for Environment, Food and Rural Affairs (2001) *The Draft Soil Strategy for England - A Consultation Paper*

Department for Environment, Food and Rural Affairs (2002) *Sustainable Food and Farming: Working Together*

Royal Commission on Environmental Pollution (1996) *The Sustainable Use of Soil*

European Commission Directorate-General Environment (2001) *The Soil Protection Communication*

10. Forestry

Steve Robertson, East Ayrshire Woodlands

We would like to thank the Institute of Chartered Foresters, the Royal Forestry Society and the Forestry Commission for kindly allowing information from their websites to be used in this chapter.

The Sector

Forestry is defined as "the science and practice of managing forests and woodlands". But modern multi-purpose forestry is about far more than just growing trees for timber: it embraces everything from planting and managing large coniferous forests to creating and tending small broadleaved woodlands, raising young trees in nurseries and felling and delivering timber to wood-using industries.

With modern multi-purpose forestry, at all levels, the forestry staff's remit is broader than ever. Forestry is now seen to have a far wider range of objectives. Instead of the focus being primarily on timber production, principal objectives now include amenity, recreation, conservation, shelter for animals and crops as well as, crucially, working with communities to achieve these goals. Woods and forests are now managed therefore to offer multiple benefits for the economy, the environment and for society as a whole.

Whilst this chapter focuses on Forestry, it also refers to Arboriculture, a related sector which has many elements and skills in common. Arboriculture is the science and practice of managing trees and woodlands as amenities, primarily for the conservation of both the rural landscape and the urban environment. Further information on careers in arboriculture can be found on several of the websites listed in the Contacts section at the end of this chapter.

Sector Profile

The Forestry Commission (FC) is the government department responsible for the protection and expansion of Britain's forests and woodlands. Its 'Forest Employment Survey 1998/9' (Forestry Commission, 2001) found that Britain's forests and woodlands directly provided 29,500 jobs in the forestry and primary wood-processing industries. There were around 14,700 jobs in England, 10,700 in Scotland and 4,100 in Wales. The Forestry Commission itself employed around 13% of the sector, private estates 29%, and the wood-processing industry 36%, with the balance working for other employers such as forest management companies and contractors.

Current research shows that the number of women employed in the Forestry sector is low, but increasing, with many women now holding key roles, particularly in forest management and research.

Over the last 40 to 50 years, much work has been done to develop the timber resource in the UK through extensive planting of conifers. As these forests have matured, timber production has doubled over the past 15 years and is set to double again over the next 15 years. This will bring with it many challenges to further develop the wood processing sector and to 'restructure' first rotation plantation forests. With almost 30,000 people employed in forestry and wood processing, the sector is an increasingly important player in the environmental jobs market.

Typical Post Names

Forest Manager/Forester, Forestry Supervisor/Foreman, Forestry Worker/Craftsman/Contractor, Community Forester, Community Liaison Officer, Civil/Mechanical Engineer, Land Agent, Landscape Architect, Researcher, Scientist

Main Employers

Forestry Commission, forest management companies, private estates, land agency firms, timber companies, consultancies, local authorities, non-governmental organisations (NGOs)

Career Opportunities

There are various possible entry or starting points in the sector, depending on your qualifications and what your goals are. Examples of the work involved and qualifications required for some of the most common posts are given below (N.B. Many qualifications mentioned here are abbreviated: please refer to the glossary at the end of the book for full titles).

Forest Manager
Managers are involved in planning and controlling a wide range of forest operations whilst safeguarding the natural environment and features of significance for nature conservation. In addition they manage public access and recreation within the forest. They may oversee one or more supervisors; be responsible for a number of direct employees or self-employed contractors; commission or plan research; deal with Health and Safety and other legislation; support woodland management by administering grants and licences including inspecting planting schemes; deal with tree preservation orders (TPOs); and carry out valuations and purchase or sell timber and other woodland produce.

Employment opportunities for forest managers exist in government departments, agencies and forest management companies, private estates, land agency firms, timber companies and consultancies. In larger organisations there may be opportunities to specialise in recreation, conservation, training, research, harvesting and the processing of timber.

A university degree and/or professional qualification (Chartered Forester), Higher National Diploma or Level 4 Vocational Qualification (VQ) will usually be required for management level posts. Postgraduate qualifications are also useful.

Forestry Supervisor/Foreman
These posts require competence to carry out a range of practical jobs and the ability to organise and supervise others undertaking them. They involve the implementation of instructions from managers and could include any of the following: laying out planting schemes, ordering materials, completing timesheets, work measurement, timber marking, measurement and dispatch, inspection of plantations plus many other tasks.

Employment at this level will usually require technical training and Vocational Qualifications: a Level 3 Vocational Qualification or the equivalent Edexcel (formerly BTEC) or Scottish Qualifications Authority (SQA - formerly SCOTVEC) certificates or diplomas in Forestry.

Forestry Workers/Craftsmen/Contractors
Those employed as forestry workers, craftsmen or contractors are increasingly expected to have a high level of skill due to expanding mechanisation and the need to run their own business as self-employed contractors. The type of work available will depend on the part of the country and the system of land management being practised in that area. It can include tree planting, maintenance, thinning and felling of trees using chainsaws or harvesting machines, road building, fencing, sawing timber, cutting coppice and preparing other woodland produce.

Normally no academic qualifications are required to start, but attainment of Vocational Qualifications (VQs) or a similar Craft Skills award through approved training and practice is essential. Skills such as communication, numeracy and interpersonal relations are desirable.

Qualifications & Work Experience
A range of qualifications are on offer, broadly split into vocational and academic. *Vocational Qualifications (VQs)* are offered by a number of colleges, through full or part-time courses. Full details of all vocational qualifications in forestry and arboriculture and other training courses may be obtained from Lantra, the Sector Skills Council for the environmental and land-based sector - their contact details are given at the end of this chapter.

There is also a wide variety of forestry *diploma* and *degree courses* offered by universities and colleges throughout the UK. *Diploma courses* are 3-year sandwich courses leading to a National Diploma or Higher National Diploma (HND) from Edexcel or SQA. Many *degree courses* embrace elements of environmental management, conservation and other disciplines relating to forestry and arboriculture. Some students do a sandwich year - often overseas - to get hands-on forestry experience. *Postgraduate courses* in forestry and similar subjects are also available: these include MSc degrees taught over twelve months with varying forestry content, as well as research leading to MPhil or PhD degrees.

It is beneficial to carry out *work experience* to see if tree work is really for you. Colleges and universities often ask prospective students about relevant work experience, and it will definitely improve your job prospects later. Experience may be obtained through working for forestry contractors, nurserymen, local authority parks departments, landscapers, gardeners or tree surgeons. Organisations like the National Trust, British Trust for Conservation Volunteers (BTCV) and Local County Naturalist Trusts may want volunteers.

Government funded *training schemes* for school leavers, young people and unemployed adults give a good foundation for getting a job in Forestry and for doing higher level Vocational Qualifications. They also prepare people for the working environment and allow them to learn specific industrial skills.

Issues and Trends

The UK suffered from serious deforestation during the 19th and early 20th centuries. After the Second World War, tree cover was around 5% of the total land area. It now stands at around 15%. In many comparable European countries the average is 30% or more. With much work still to do, the UK now finds itself in the position of being one of the few places in the world where tree cover is actually expanding as more and more trees are planted. Amenity tree care is moving up the agenda too, and new disciplines such as Urban, Amenity, Environmental and Social Forestry are emerging.

Re-afforestation is also helped by initiatives such as the Community Forests in England, and the Central Scotland Forest in Scotland. In Scotland, the phenomenon of genuine 'Community Woods', owned and managed by community members, has really taken off, with a database of over 80 woodlands in or approaching this category of ownership. In Wales, much work has been done by organisations such as Coed Cymru to promote greater expansion and use of small woodland, and by Forest Enterprise and the National Assembly in the use of woodlands as an educational resource.

Throughout the UK, the Forestry Commission's Forest Education Initiative has been a force behind the development of woodlands as a teaching resource. See the Forestry Commission website (details in Contacts section) for more information.

There are opportunities for British trained foresters to work abroad, e.g. for UK government, non-government agencies and voluntary organisations.

Personal Profiles

Steve Robertson - Community Liaison Officer/Forester, East Ayrshire Woodlands

"I started my forestry career as a self-employed tree planter and estate worker for Fountain Forestry, after doing a variety of voluntary conservation work for the National Trust. I went on to study for two years for an HND in Forest Management at the Scottish School of Forestry in Inverness. I left without completing the course to work as a contractor in Norway, extracting timber by horse from the huge forests in the east of the country.

Having a strong desire to study in some form, however, I returned to take a Languages degree at Aberdeen University, whilst working part-time as a forestry contractor on farm woodland establishment projects in Aberdeenshire. I followed this with a Masters Degree in Rural Planning (Environmental Management), again at the University of Aberdeen. The Masters course was particularly brilliant, especially the team building and community working skills which I gained.

Over the next two years I worked for a variety of community forestry and rural research projects including contracts to the Scottish Executive, Universities and private consultants. One great benefit of freelance work was the ability to choose exactly who I worked for, developing my knowledge and skills in the particular area of community forestry work that I chose.

I now work for East Ayrshire Woodlands, a partnership project attached to the Local Authority, as a Community Forester. The work includes design of new woodland sites and management of existing woods for various owners. My job also includes developing links between local people and local woods and engaging young people with woodlands via the Forest Education Initiative. I also work in partnership with other conservation bodies such as Scottish Natural Heritage and the Farming and Wildlife Advisory Group on projects such as a district-wide Red Squirrel initiative and individual farm and woodland walks and events. Aspects of my job do allow me to spend some time out in the woods and forest, but most of the time I'm in the office. Whilst it's hard, with such a demanding remit, to complete all projects to the standard which I'd like, it is very satisfying to have great flexibility to choose how to bring projects forward and how to use my existing skills to the maximum.

My career path could have been much simpler. I could have stuck to more directly relevant courses and completed that first HND! However, all of my experience and qualifications have been important stages in getting me to where I am now."

Nigel Petts - Woodland Officer, Coed Cymru

"After 3 years as a self-employed forestry contractor I enrolled on the Scottish School of Forestry's HND Forestry course, gaining my diploma in 1992. I then worked on self-employed contracts for private estates before being employed by the Forestry Commission as harvesting and marketing Forest Officer where I was in charge of 16 mechanised harvesting operatives.

In 1995 I started work with Coed Cymru as their Woodland Officer for Ceredigion. Coed Cymru was set up to help safeguard Wales' native woodland heritage through the implementation of continual cover silviculture. We encourage landowners to sustainably manage neglected broadleaf woodlands by offering help and advice with woodland management, Native Woodland Plans, Woodland Grant Schemes, marking and measuring thinnings, coordinating contractors, adding value and marketing any end produce. To this end I am often found extolling the virtues of using local timber to practically everyone who might be involved in buying timber for both the public and private sector.

The diversity of this job has forced me to broaden my horizons and develop a new range of skills. As well as knowledge of the timber sector, we have to be able to assess how our work affects all aspects of woodland ecology and manage accordingly. It's a very demanding but rewarding role and the one thing you can guarantee is that all sites are different and most are "challenging" to say the least."

Contacts

Qualifications and Training

City & Guilds London Institute
1 Giltspur Street, London, EC1A 9DD
Tel: 020 7294 2800; Fax: 020 7294 2405
www.city-and-guilds.co.uk

Edexcel Foundation - Edexcel incorporates BTEC qualifications
Stewart House, 32 Russell Square, London, WC1B 5ON
Tel: 0870 240 9800; Fax: 020 7758 6960
www.edexcel.org.uk

Lantra - for details of Vocational Qualifications and other training courses
Lantra House, NAC, Kenilworth, Warwickshire, CV8 2LG
Tel: 0845 707 8007;   Fax: 024 7669 6732
E-mail: nto@lantra.co.uk
www.lantra.co.uk

National Proficiency Tests Council (NPTC) - for details of local centres offering
Vocational Qualifications
National Agricultural Centre, Stoneleigh, Kenilworth, Warwickshire, CV8 2LG
Tel: 024 7669 6553; Fax: 024 7669 6128
www.nptc.org.uk

Scottish Qualifications Authority (SQA) - incorporates SCOTVEC qualifications
The Helpdesk, Hanover House, 24 Douglas Street, Glasgow, G2 7NQ
Tel: 0141 242 2214; Fax: 0141 242 2244
www.sqa.org.uk

Universities

University of Aberdeen
Department of Agriculture & Forestry, University of Aberdeen, MacRobert
Building, 581 King Street, Aberdeen, AB24 5UA
Tel: 01224-274122; Fax: 01224 273731
E-mail: agfor@abdn.ac.uk
www.abdn.ac.uk/agfor

University of Edinburgh
School of Forestry, Institute of Ecology and Resource Management (IERM),
Darwin Building, Mayfield Road, Edinburgh, EH9 3JU
Tel: 0131 650 5420; Fax: 0131 662 0478
E-mail: ierm.darwin@ed.ac.uk
www.helios.bto.ed.ac.uk/ierm/

University of Oxford
Oxford Forestry Institute, Department of Plant Sciences, South Parks Road,
Oxford, OX1 3RB
Tel: 01865 275 070; Fax: 01865 2275 074
www.plants.ox.ac.uk/ofi/

University of Wales, Bangor
School of Agricultural and Forest Sciences, Gwynedd, LL57 2UW
Tel: 01248 351 151; Fax: 01248 354 997
www.safs.bangor.ac.uk

University of Central Lancashire
Newton Rigg Campus, Penrith, Cumbria
Tel: 01768 863 791; Fax: 01768 867 249
E-mail: info@newtonrigg.ac.uk
www.newtonrigg.ac.uk

Inverness College
Scottish School of Forestry, Balloch, Inverness-shire
Tel: 01463 273 600; Fax: 01463 792 497
E-mail: stewart_brougham@groupwise.uhi.ac.uk
www.uhi.ac.uk/inverness

University College Dublin
Department of Crop Science, Horticulture & Forestry, Faculty of Agriculture,
Belfield, Dublin 4, Ireland

Tel: +353 1 706 7756; Fax: +353 1 706 1104
E-mail: Valerie.Guilfoyle@ucd.ie
www.ucd.ie/~agri

Other contacts

Arboricultural Association
Ampfield House, Ampfield, Nr Romsey, Hampshire, SO51 9PA
Tel: 01794 368717; Fax: 01794 368978;
E-mail: treehouse@dial.pipex.com
www.trees.org.uk

Coed Cymru
The Old Sawmill, Tregynon, Newtown, Powys, SY16 3PL
Tel: 01686 650 777; Fax: 01686 650 696
E-mail: coedcymru@mid-wales.net
www.coedcymru.mid-wales.net

Forestry Commission (Personnel Services)
231 Corstorphine Road, Edinburgh, EH12 7AT
Tel: 0131 334 0303; Fax: 0131 334 3047
E-mail: enquiries@forestry.gsi.gov.uk
www.forestry.gov.uk

Forestry Commission Personnel (Research)
Forest Research Station, Alice Holt Lodge, Wrecclesham, Farnham, Surrey,
GU10 4LH
Tel: 01420 22255

Forest Service (Northern Ireland)
Dundonald House, Upper Newtownards Road, Belfast, BT4 3SB
Tel: 02890 524480; Fax: 2890 524570
www.forestserviceni.gov.uk

Highland Birchwoods
Training Contact: Alan Mackintosh
Littleburn, Munlochy, Ross-shire, IV8 8NN
Tel: 01463 811606; Fax:01463 811607
E-mail: alan@highlandbirchwoods.co.uk
www.caledonian-partnership.org.uk

Institute of Chartered Foresters
7a St Colme Street, Edinburgh, EH3 6AA
Tel: 0131 225 2705; Fax: 0131 220 6128
E-mail: icf@charteredforesters.org
www.charteredforesters.org

Reforesting Scotland
Training Contact: Nick Marshall
62-66 Newhaven Road, Edinburgh, EH6 5BQ
Tel: 0131 554 4321; Fax: 0131 554 0088
E-mail: reforscot@gn.apc.org
www.reforestingscotland.org

Royal Forestry Society of England, Wales & Northern Ireland
102 High Street, Tring, Hertfordshire, HP23 4AF
Tel: 01442 822028; Fax: 01442 890395
E-mail: rfshq@rfs.org.uk
www.rfs.org.uk

Royal Scottish Forestry Society (RSFS)
Hagg-on-Esk, Canonbie, Dumfriesshire, DG14 0XE
Tel: 01387 371518; Fax : 01387 371418
E-mail: rsfs@ednet.co.uk
www.rsfs.org

The Tree Council
51 Catherine Place, London, SW1E 6DY
Tel: 020 7828 9928; Fax: 020 7828 9060
www.treecouncil.org.uk

Publications

Forestry and British Timber (monthly forestry journal)
Reforesting Scotland (quarterly alternative forestry journal)
Timber Grower (timber trade journal)

References

Forestry Commission (2001) *Forest Employment Survey 1998/9: Employment in Forestry and Primary Wood Processing*

11. Fisheries

Justin Taberham, CIWEM, based on text provided by the Institute of Fisheries Management (IFM)

The Sector

Fisheries careers are very varied, but for ease of understanding we have split the Fisheries sector into 'Fish Farming' and 'Other Fisheries Work'.

The Fisheries sector is extremely popular - possibly due to the romantic notion that a hobby like fishing can become a career. Whilst this is true, most jobs in fisheries are very hard work and involve unsociable hours working in all weathers.

The sector employs around 3000 people in the UK, mainly in government agencies, water companies, environmental and engineering consultancies, as well as fish farming companies.

Fish Farming
One attraction of fish farming to many is the idea of working with fish in a rural environment. But there are certain disadvantages:
·   Many fish farms are remote and isolated, with little suitable housing in the vicinity; this will apply especially with the growing number of marine fish farms.
·   The fish need to be tended seven days a week.
·   Tasks which are fun on a summer's day can be really unpleasant in a midwinter gale.
·   Large-scale fish farming is a relatively new industry in Great Britain and suffers from many of the ills which beset other new businesses such as poor working conditions and minimal job security.

Other Fisheries Work
The Environment Agency employs Fisheries Officers or Inspectors/Water Bailiffs who carry out a range of duties including enforcement work (patrolling, checking licences), carrying out fish population surveys, attending fish mortalities and carrying out fish rescues and transfers. Increasingly, fisheries staff are managing habitat enhancement projects.

Fisheries Officers manage teams of Inspectors and/or Bailiffs. A number of Fisheries Scientists/Officers provide the scientific support for this work. Bailiffs are also employed by riparian owners to maintain their own fisheries.

An increasing number of people seeking employment in the fisheries field are being engaged by consultancies carrying out Environmental Impact Assessment (EIA) and other environmental management work.

Typical Post Names

Fisheries Officer, Fisheries Manager, Fisheries Scientist, Hatchery Manager, Fisheries Consultant, Inspector/ Water Bailiff

Main Employers

Environment Agency (EA), Scottish Environment Protection Agency (SEPA),

Environmental Consultancies, Department for Environment, Food & Rural Affairs (DEFRA), Centre for Environment, Fisheries and Aquaculture Science (CEFAS), Fish Farming Companies

Career Opportunities

The Environment Agency employs the largest number of people in freshwater fisheries work in Britain. Other employers include the Department for Environment, Food & Rural Affairs (DEFRA), the Freshwater Biological Association, the Scottish Office Agriculture Environment & Fisheries Department (SOAEFD) some Salmon District Fisheries Boards, the Scottish Environment Protection Agency (SEPA), the Fisheries Department of the Department of Agriculture and Rural Development (DARD) for Northern Ireland, The Foyle Fisheries Commission, various Universities, local authorities and private enterprise including consultants and commercial fish farms.

The majority of fish farming concerns are small with owners doing much of the work themselves. There are thought to be in excess of 500 fish farms of one sort or another in the British Isles, with many salmon sea cage farms in Scotland and on the West Coast of Ireland.

On the marine side of fisheries the points of entry into a career are as diverse as the freshwater side, entry being dependent on qualifications and experience.

The Institute of Fisheries Management (IFM) has produced a simple generalised career structure in fisheries which, with only minor modification, is applicable to the staff structures of most employing bodies. This career structure is found in the IFM leaflet 'Careers in Fisheries'.

Generally it is advisable to obtain the highest qualifications that you can before seeking permanent employment in the fisheries field. Any opportunity to gain practical experience should be taken.

Many of those keen to enter fisheries have undertaken a biological course, usually to first degree level, although some are still at school and others (ex-servicemen in particular) are seeking new careers. Most of the positions for qualified staff go to biologists with specialist post-graduate training or fisheries experience.

Prospective candidates who can reinforce their biological knowledge with other relevant skills will be viewed most favourably by employers. Such skills may include:
·   Experience of practical fisheries management, such as may be obtained by participation in an Angling Club work party
·   Training and experience in practical tasks - many fish farmers have to carry out varied maintenance work
·   Livestock husbandry experience
·   Having a full driving licence - this can mean the difference between getting a job and not, particularly at the lower entry points
·   Good interview skills - these are important!

Anyone considering further training prior to entering fisheries can either undertake general training in practical skills or specialist courses related to fisheries. The IFM leaflet 'Careers in Fisheries' has a full list of fisheries-related courses in the UK and Europe. See the Contacts section at the end of the chapter for a list of organisations offering related courses.

Opportunities for fisheries research may also occur at the CEFAS Fisheries Laboratory at Lowestoft, the SOAEFD Laboratory at Pitlochry, the Scottish Association for Marine Science at Oban, the Freshwater Biological Association at Windermere and with the Environment Agency.

Major employing bodies advertise all vacancies in the national press (particularly in the Guardian, the Telegraph, the Times, New Scientist and Fish Farmer). Other posts are often advertised locally and in the angling press. Many fish farmers advertise vacancies in the bimonthly magazines Fish Farmer and Fish Farming International.

Issues and Trends

Fisheries careers are very popular. There are currently far more people attempting to obtain employment in this field than there are suitable openings, particularly at the lower entry points. While numbers employed in water companies are fairly stable, there is growth in the public sector and in consultancy.

There are many issues which will impact on the fisheries sector, including the EC Water Framework Directive, under which river catchments will be assessed for their ecological status.

There are issues which may alter or threaten fisheries resources or the need for specialist staff. These include:

- Concerns over the environmental impacts of commercial fish farming
- Introduced fish diseases through increases in live fish imports
- Increased commercialism, especially of stillwater fisheries, which provide a resource for anglers but may threaten the ecological status of waters and increase the possibility of novel fish disease transmission, ill health and mortalities
- Lack of clarity over the role of fisheries agencies in angling where there is a fishery science versus fishing issue. A high quality fishery doesn't necessarily mean good fishing!
- Introduction of new species, either legally or illegally. This practice will inevitably have environmental impacts

Personal Profiles

Dr Keith Hendry - Managing Director & Senior Fish Biologist, APEM Ltd

"I can trace my interest in pursuing a career in fisheries a very long way. I come from a fishing background, my family in Scotland being trawler men from the east coast, so I have always been surrounded by fish, fishing and fishermen of one type or another. I was fascinated by fish from a very early age, and wanted to work in fisheries for as long as I can remember.

My first degree was at Plymouth Polytechnic, which was the smallest Poly in the country back in 1979 but offered that all important fisheries science bias to their Biological Sciences degree course. It was an excellent three years covering both marine and freshwater fisheries and provided me with a strong base from which to progress. My first career break came immediately after my Finals. Through being in the right place at the right time I landed a seasonal job as a research diver at the Marine Biological Association in Plymouth - this was great practical experience, including diving, specimen collecting and carrying out underwater surveys. Following a brief stint in casual jobs in Warwickshire, I returned to the South West working in forestry for a year before getting my second big break as a Fisheries Technician for the South West Water Authority in the mid 1980s on the Roadford Dam project. The work involved all manner of field investigations into salmonid population biology and migration, including electric fishing, trapping, radio telemetry, fish ageing, data management and so on. The amount of experience I gained in my three years was immense but at that time prior to Water Company privatisation, opportunities for advancement were few, so I decided to take my future into my own hands and take the first tentative steps into consultancy.

In 1987 I joined Manchester University as a Research Associate to service their contract research projects and undertake a PhD. It was hard going as I had to be financially self-sufficient after the first year. I finished my PhD in 1990 and formed APEM as a Limited Company, leaving the University in 1991. Since then it has been a case of slowly growing the consultancy, but ensuring that we stick to the world of fisheries and aquatic science. There are now 14 people employed by the company, all of us aquatic scientists of one form or another. Maintaining my focus on fisheries science and keeping true to my early ambition to work in this field has been fundamental to the success of APEM. We have developed an excellent reputation as a niche consultancy specialising in fisheries, and for me this has been the realisation of what I consider to be the ultimate career. Maintaining professional interests away from consultancy has been important, two pinnacles of achievement being nominated a member of the Governments' Salmon and Freshwater Fisheries Review Committee and being awarded the status of Fellow by the Institute of Fisheries Management, an extremely important body for anyone interested in pursuing a career in fisheries."

Nigel Hewlett - Team Leader Fisheries Scientist, Environment Agency National Fisheries Laboratory

"My interest in fisheries stems from being an angler, which led me to do a degree in Fisheries (rather than economics!). The main value of my degree, however, came from the sandwich year which I spent at the former National Rivers Authority (NRA) fisheries laboratory in York. There I gained experience in fish health and fish ageing, which led to me joining the Environment Agency (EA) in 1996 as a Technical Assistant doing similar work. In 1998 I gained the post of Assistant Fisheries Scientist at the National Fisheries Laboratory with particular responsibility for the running of the microbiology lab. I was promoted to the post of Team Leader Fisheries Scientist late in 1999.

As Team Leader Fisheries Scientist, I manage a team of scientists who undertake health checks on fish to be moved to, or within, still and/or running water to prevent the spread of parasites and diseases. The team also carries out investigations of fish mortalities in the wild and is involved in a number of other fish health related projects. I am also required to advise the fisheries function within the EA on issues relating to the transfer of fish disease and disease outbreaks.

The main difficulty with getting employment with the EA at that time was the number of good candidates chasing a limited number of jobs. The post I eventually got was at the third attempt. The best part of my job is the blend of management and technical work I am able to do. It is also very rewarding to contribute to the EA's policies on fish health, see real benefits to the environment and talk to fishery owners who have benefited from our advice."

Ben Bayliss - Fisheries Scientist, Environment Agency

"My interest in fish and all things fishy began at a young age. At the tender age of 5 I had my first fishing adventure on my local river, the River Kent in Cumbria, and was hooked! Fishing became my hobby and took up much of my free time during my school years. I began fishing for brown trout but soon moved on to salmon, sea trout and other species found in the lakes and rivers of the Lake District. I decided during my 'O' Levels that I would like to pursue a career with an environmental basis, and preferably one which involved fish and fisheries. They say mixing business with pleasure is a 'no-no' but in my case I couldn't think of anything else I'd rather do!

After taking advice from my careers adviser at school, I opted to take Chemistry and Biology at 'A' Level to give me a good scientific basis to take onto my further education. I investigated various opportunities at Degree level, including aquaculture and marine/oceanography courses. Although some parts of these courses were of interest, I eventually decided on Plymouth University and an Honours Degree in Fisheries Science. This particular degree course allowed me to select various modules and tailor the course to my requirements. The degree encompassed subject areas from fish biology to the Common Fisheries Policy and gave me a good broad-based knowledge.

During my summer breaks from University I took summer jobs at the National Rivers Authority (NRA - the Environment Agency's predecessor) working with the Fisheries department. My work during this time concentrated on juvenile fish surveys, radio tracking fish and report writing. The combination of field and office based work was precisely what I was looking for in terms of my future career. Upon completion of my Degree I took temporary contract work again with the NRA and subsequently the Environment Agency (EA), primarily working on specific projects involving tagging and tracking salmon and sea trout through estuary and river systems.

In 1997 I was fortunate enough to obtain a permanent job with the EA as a Fisheries Scientist. My job is very varied. I have responsibility for fisheries science carried out by the EA in South Cumbria. This work includes juvenile fish surveys, the production of Salmon Action Plans (SAPs), collecting and interpreting fish counter data, providing sound scientific advice for fisheries management and development, and project work. My time is split between the field and office and I'm sure it's the variety and importance of this work that maintains my enthusiasm for what I feel is my ideal job."

Contacts

CEFAS Lowestoft Laboratory
Pakefield Road, Lowestoft, Suffolk, NR33 0HT
Tel: 01502 562244; Fax: 01502 513865
www.cefas.co.uk/Lowestoftlab.htm

The Chartered Institution of Water and Environmental Management (CIWEM)
www.ciwem.com

Environment Agency
www.environment-agency.gov.uk

Fish Farmer magazine
PO Box 535, Addlestone, KT15 1FA
www.fishfarmer-magazine.com

Freshwater Biological Association
The Ferry House, Ambleside, Cumbria, LA22 0LP
Tel: 015394 42468; Fax: 015394 46914
www.fba.org.uk

Institute of Fisheries Management (IFM)
Ian Dolben, Careers Officer, 36 Kensington Road, Rawcliffe, York, YO30 5XG
Tel: 01904 630673
E-mail: ian_dolben@lineone.net
Anyone wishing to join the Institute should contact the Membership Secretary, 39
Chelveston Road, Raunds, Northants NN9 6DA
www.ifm.org.uk

National Farmers Union (NFU)
The NFU maintains a register of those interested in jobs in fish farming. Contact the
Secretary, Fish Farming Committee, NFU, Agriculture House, Knightsbridge, London
SW1X 7NJ.

Scottish Environment Protection Agency (SEPA)
www.sepa.org.uk

SOAEFD Freshwater Fisheries Laboratory
Faskally, Pitlochry, Perthshire, PH16 5LB
Tel: 01796 472060; Fax: 1796 473523
www.fishlink.com/ti/151/

The Scottish Salmon Growers Association produces 'Training Opportunities for
Fish Farmers', a booklet containing full details of fish farming training courses. This
is available from SSGA, Drummond House, Scott Street, Perth PH1 5EJ

Voluntary Service Overseas
VSO, 317 Putney Bridge Road, London SW15 2PN
www.vso.org.uk

Organisations offering Fisheries-Related Courses

Barony College
Parkgate, Dumfries, DG1 3NE
Tel: 01387 860251; Fax: 01387 860395
E-mail: admin@barony.ac.uk
www.barony.ac.uk

Bishop Burton College
Bishop Burton, Beverley, North Humberside, HU17 8QG
Tel: 01964 550481; Fax: 01964 551190

Brooksby Melton College
Melton Mowbray, Leicestershire LE14 2LJ
Tel: 01664 434291; Fax 01664 434572
E-mail: enquire@brooksby.ac.uk
www.brooksby.ac.uk

Broomfield College
Derbyshire College of Agriculture and Horticulture, Morley, Ilkeston, Derbyshire,
DE7 6DN
Tel: 01332 836600; Fax 01332 836601

Institute of Fisheries Management (IFM)
IFM has two Correspondence Courses - their Certificate and Diploma in Fisheries
Management and Certificate in Fish Farming. These courses are valued highly by
employers in this sector, as is IFM membership. Please see the Contacts section for
their contact details.

Lews Castle College
Stornaway, Isle of Lewis, HS2 0XR
Tel: 01851 770000; Fax 01851 770001
E-mail: aofficele@groupwise.uhi.ac.uk

Merrist Wood College
Worplesdon, Guildford, Surrey
Tel: 01483 884040
www.merristwood.ac.uk

Moulton College
Moulton, Northampton, NN3 1RR
Tel: 01604 491131; Fax 01604 491127
E-mail: enquiries@moulton.ac.uk
www.moulton.ac.uk

North Atlantic Fisheries College
Port Arthur, Scalloway, Shetland Isles, ZE1 0UN
Tel: 01595 880328; Fax 01595 880549
E-mail: admin@nafc.ac.uk
www.nafc.ac.uk

Reaseheath College
Reaseheath, Nantwich, Cheshire, CW5 6DF
Tel: 01270 625131; Fax 01270 625665
E-mail: reception@reaseheath.ac.uk
www.reaseheath.ac.uk

Rodbaston College
Rodbaston, Penkridge, Stafford, ST19 5PH
Tel: 01785 712209; Fax 01785 715701
E-mail: rodenquiries@rodbaston.ac.uk
www.rodbaston.ac.uk

Sea Fish Industry Authority
Seafish is the Government-appointed National Training Organisation for the fishing,
merchanting and processing, retailing and frying sectors of the sea fish industry.

Seafish Training & Standards Division, Seafish House, St. Andrews Dock, Hull, HU3 4QE
Tel: 01482 327837; Fax: 01482 223310
E-mail: training@seafish.co.uk
www.seafish.co.uk

Sparsholt College Hampshire
Sparsholt, Winchester, Hampshire, SO21 2NF
Tel: 01962 776441; Fax 01962 776587
E-mail: enquiry@sparsholt.ac.uk

12. Waterways

Kate Griffin, British Waterways

The Sector

Britain's 200 year old inland waterway network grew to serve the industries and factories that powered Britain through the Industrial Revolution. At its height, the network comprised more than 5,000 miles (8,046km) of canals and navigable rivers in England, Scotland and Wales.

Today some 3,000 miles (4,828km) of these historic waterways survive. British Waterways cares for just over 2,000 miles of inland waterways, with others managed and owned by a range of organisations, authorities and trusts, including the Environment Agency, which manages 600 miles (966km) of inland waterways, mainly river navigations.

Conserving, restoring and regenerating the inland waterway network is certainly a challenge - especially as it is of such great environmental and historic importance. The waterways feature thousands of significant structures, from simple locks and bridges to complex tunnels and soaring aqueducts - most of these are Scheduled Ancient Monuments or are listed. Waterways are also home to many Sites of Special Scientific Interest, sheltering rare species including water voles, bats, birds, butterflies and unique plants like Floating Water Plantain and Bennett's Pondweed.

Increasingly Britain's waterways are playing a key role in urban and rural regeneration. Inland waterways provide an important leisure and recreational resource, attracting millions of visitors each year including boaters, walkers, cyclists, anglers, nature lovers, history enthusiasts and those seeking respite from the hustle and bustle of city life.

Ensuring that the inland waterways are safeguarded for future generations to enjoy is the key challenge facing this sector today.

Sector Profile

Far from being the forgotten backwaters of major towns and cities, waterways are being rediscovered and re-invented as places where people want to live, work, relax and socialise.

This is a period of renaissance and optimism for Britain's inland waterways with major restoration and regeneration projects taking place across the country in both urban and rural areas. This expansion is creating important employment opportunities along the entire network as waterways are re-invented for the 21st century. The new focus on waterway renewal is leading to the creation of jobs in a wide range of areas - environment, landscaping, engineering, construction, waterway management, water management and the provision of visitor attractions.

Not surprisingly, water is the key to the business of this sector and its management involves a wide range of skills and expertise. It's very much a team effort!

Key Organisations

British Waterways, a public corporation, works with a broad range of public, private and voluntary sector partners to use the inland waterways to deliver social, economic and environmental benefits to local communities and create a sustainable future for the waterways. British Waterways currently employs just over 2,000 people.

The Waterways Trust is a national charity established in 1999 to promote greater public enjoyment and awareness of the UK's canals and rivers. The Trust works to develop partnerships to secure funding for the conservation and restoration of waterways, and to help realise the social, educational, environmental and economic potential of living waterways. The Waterways Trust currently employs approximately 100 people, many of whom work in its waterways museums.

The *Inland Waterways Association (IWA)* is a registered charity with approximately 17,000 members. It was formed in 1946 to ensure the retention, conservation, restoration and development of Britain's inland waterways. IWA believes that rivers and canals should be used for commercial and leisure boating and many other activities including education, canoeing, angling and towing path walking. IWA currently employs 10 people who co-ordinate the work of the volunteers of the Association.

The Broads Authority was set up in 1989 to conserve and enhance the natural beauty of the Norfolk and Suffolk Broads, promote enjoyment of this special landscape and protect the interests of navigation. The Broads is a unique area of water, grazing marshes, fen and woodland and is Britain's largest protected wetland, with similar status to a national park. The Broads Authority currently employs 97 full time staff and 26 seasonal staff.

The *Environment Agency* also employs many people in this sector working across a range of disciplines.

Typical Post Names

British Waterways
Waterway Operative, Waterway Supervisor, Waterway Manager, Waterway Engineer, Environmental Advisor, Landscape Architect, Safety Advisor, Craft Specialist, Hydrologist, Lands Surveyor, Waterway Ecologist, Water Quality Scientist, Waste Manager, Environmental Scientist, Heritage Officer, Planning Officer.

The Waterways Trust
Project Liaison Manager, Volunteer Co-ordinator, Communications Manager, Grants & Trusts Development Manager, Marketing Manager, Curator, Head of Archives and Records, Boat and Engineering Manager, Visitor Services Manager, Museum Assistant.

Inland Waterways Association
Project Officer, Campaigns Officer, Public Affairs Officer, Membership Officer.

The Broads Authority
Navigation Ranger, Countryside Ranger, Navigation Works Technician, Project Technician, Seasonal Navigation Quay Ranger, Conservation Officer, Marshman.

Main Employers

British Waterways, Environment Agency, The Waterways Trust, Inland Waterways Association, The Broads Authority

Career Opportunities

Waterways provide a wide range of career opportunities spanning diverse interests and disciplines. From environment to heritage, from engineering to landscape design, from visitor attraction development to water management - there is plenty of scope for involvement. For this reason the qualifications required at entry level are varied.

Maintenance
Caring for Britain's waterways in the everyday practical sense offers the opportunity to make a real contribution on the canal or river bank. Most of the infrastructure is man-made and over 200 years old, and it needs tender loving care!

Canals and river navigations need a controlled supply of water to keep them full without spilling over. This requires skill and judgement backed up with modern technology and expertise.

To enable boats to navigate the waterways there must be a clear channel deep enough to allow safe passage. Clearance of silt, overhanging trees and flotsam are vital tasks. In addition towpaths are regularly used by walkers, cyclists and anglers and they expect them to be maintained in good, attractive condition with clear access. There is tremendous opportunity for people to enjoy fulfilling and rewarding work, caring for this unique environment.

For example, the duties of a *Waterway Operative* are varied and include water control, canal maintenance, grass cutting, lock keeping and customer care. Previous experience from a building or agricultural background is desirable. *Craft Specialists* are employed in skilled work manufacturing lock gates and other unique waterway items. City and Guilds craft qualifications are required.

Engineering
Waterway engineers play a vital role in securing a safe and attractive environment, both for the people who visit the waterways and the wildlife that inhabits them. They also have to find innovative, modern solutions to old and new waterway challenges, such as differences in canal levels. In Scotland, the recently opened Falkirk Wheel boat lift, linking the newly restored Forth & Clyde and Union canals, is a breathtaking example of the futuristic design and imaginative engineering that is defining waterways for the 21st century. Engineers are not confined to working on any particular type of waterway or structure, which means that flexibility and organisational skills are important.

Typical posts include: Project Engineer, Graduate Engineer, Waterways Engineer, Assistant Engineer, Electrical Engineer, Senior Projects Engineer. In British Waterways, vacancies occasionally arise for Graduate or Chartered Engineers at waterway and regional offices.

Water Management
The complex waterway network has to be managed to maintain high standards of supply for customers including boaters, commercial abstractors and marina owners, while respecting the unique natural environment. In terms of available water British Waterways would rank in the top five water companies in England and Wales. This commitment means ensuring enough water during times of drought and reducing the risks to customers and infrastructure during times of flood.

Where spare water is available without causing environmental stress, it is sold to industry under licence from the Environment Agency.

From technical experts in the water management team to water controllers on the canal bank, there are many exciting opportunities for people who are interested in a high level of responsibility and enjoy working with the environment. Typical posts include: Hydrologist, Hydrometric Assistant, Hydraulic Modeller, Water Controller, Water Sales Executive, Reservoir Keeper.

Architecture, Environment and Heritage
This sector of waterway work covers heritage and landscape, planning and design, nature conservation, biodiversity, water quality management, waste management, environmental science and sustainable development.

Conserving, restoring and developing a network of such environmental and historic importance is a challenge, requiring a team of dedicated specialists to manage and balance both natural and built heritage and waterway landscapes.

In British Waterways, specialists advise staff at all levels on policy and work closely with other statutory bodies to influence national policy and its implementation. Experts also work with teams on the ground to help develop the waterways in a sustainable way.

Professional qualifications and experience are required for roles which include: Landscape Architect, Planner, Urban Designer, Design Architect, Ecologist, Environmental Advisor, Geographical Information Systems (GIS) Assistant, Waste Manager, Water Quality Scientist, Environmental Scientist.

Estates and Surveying
Because of the extensive land and building portfolio surrounding the waterways, significant opportunities exist in property management. In Estates and Surveying in British Waterways, property professionals ensure effective management and continual development of the property portfolio, maximising revenue while enhancing the surrounding waterway environment. This includes more than 2,800 listed buildings, more than 130 Scheduled Ancient Monuments, 1,000 wildlife conservation sites and over 100 Sites of Special Scientific Interest.

Possible opportunities include: Lands Surveyor, Commercial Surveyor, Estates Officer, Development Surveyor, Property Manager, Property Management Surveyor.

Salaries
British Waterways, the largest employer in this field, aims to offer overall salary levels at the median (middle) of the national employment marketplace, coupled with an attractive benefits package and excellent working environment.

Issues and Trends

Renewal and Restoration
Britain's waterways are currently entering a period of unprecedented renewal. In March 2002, the biggest ever programme of waterway restorations valued at £500 million was announced. The two-stage programme, backed by a broad range of partners and public support, covers over 300 miles of canals and waterway structures to be restored or newly built.

The first phase, to open some 220 miles of canals and structures, is due for completion in 2002. This includes the internationally significant Scheduled Ancient Monument, the Anderton Boat Lift - the first of its kind in the world, which re-opened in March 2002 after restoration, and the Falkirk Wheel in Scotland - designed for the 21st century as the world's first-ever rotating boat lift.

A programme of nine further canal restorations and new waterway schemes has been announced by British Waterways in partnership with The Waterways Trust, including the first new canal to be designed for more than 100 years - the Bedford & Milton Keynes Waterway.

Government
The key factor underpinning this massive resurgence is the recognition that living, revitalised waterways bring real social, economic and environmental benefits to the communities they touch.

This was endorsed in 'Waterways for Tomorrow', the first Government policy paper on waterways for more than 30 years. Published in June 2000 by the Department for Transport, Local Government and the Regions, it specifically highlights the potential of regenerated waterways to improve the quality of life and environment for millions of people and communities throughout the country.

Freight
After their heyday 200 years ago, canals were superseded by rail and road as a means of freight transport. By the 1960s and 1970s waterways were in decline, with many sections abandoned and forgotten.

Today however, freight is making a modest return with around 3.5million tonnes carried annually on British Waterways' navigations. There is a real niche market for the carriage of non time-sensitive products such as coal, steel, aggregates and petroleum.

As pressures of pollution and road congestion grow, the Government firmly believes in the potential of the nation's waterways to reduce lorry movements where appropriate. Up to 3.5 per cent of all road freight currently carried could be transferred to waterways. In London, trials to move household refuse by waterway have been completed successfully.

Balance
Managing the delicate ecological balance of the waterways is a key consideration. Canals and rivers are a prime habitat for rare species including the endangered water vole and plants like Floating Water Plantain. An important challenge for everyone working in this sector is safeguarding the unique waterway environment and its flora and fauna, while ensuring that it is safe and sustainable for future generations to enjoy.

Leisure and Recreation

Half the population of England and Wales lives within five miles of a waterway - and with 160 million visits each year our canals, rivers, lochs, fens and broads are clearly a prime leisure and recreational asset. From boaters, both those who own their craft and those who have hired one for a holiday, to walkers, cyclists, anglers and those who are interested in environment and history, waterways are a unique national resource.

An ongoing challenge for organisations working in the field is to ensure that waterways are well maintained, attractive and accessible to all, and that a range of opportunities and facilities are provided to enhance both the landscape and the experience.

Personal Profiles

Michael Kielkowski - Assistant Engineer, British Waterways Technical Services

"Following A-Levels I went to Sheffield Hallam University to study BEng (Hons) in Civil Engineering. The third year of the course involved a placement and I was fortunate enough to get a job with British Waterways, which gave me a very comprehensive introduction to the role of engineer.

I was involved with projects on various structures, including locks and reservoirs, and had the opportunity to supervise some works carried out on the Lancaster Canal.

Subsequently, British Waterways offered me a Graduate Engineer role working on the Kennet & Avon Canal Heritage Lottery Fund Project. This had a £29 million budget to address the outstanding engineering and operational problems on the canal and restore it to its original glory while providing facilities for a 21st century leisure resource. My main responsibility was to provide engineering support to the rest of the project team, which involved producing designs, documentation and drawings, together with a lot of site based work, including supervision of a £1.5 million relining project.

I've now transferred to British Waterways' Technical Services department. There I've been able to utilise the knowledge gained while working on the Heritage Lottery Project and have been involved with a variety of schemes. I now have more responsibility, taking jobs from conception through to completion on site.

The most enjoyable aspect of my work is the variety as no two problems are the same. Working on historic structures designed by famous engineers such as Rennie and Telford gives great job satisfaction. I'm proud that future generations will enjoy spending time on sections of the canal network that I have helped to restore and enhance."

Darren Leftley - Head of Hydrology, British Waterways

"I joined British Waterways after gaining an MSc in Hydrology. In my first role I was responsible for managing two members of staff and ensuring that the measurement and monitoring of water across the network was up to British Standards. Considering that the network included England, Scotland and Wales and over 500 sites, it was certainly challenging.

My role now is much more simple - it is to ensure that there is enough water available to the waterways to meet all our future needs. I now manage the Water Management Team at British Waterways' head office in Watford. The team are experts in all aspects of canal hydrology, from modelling water movement to designing monitoring stations and advising all our clients on the proper use of water.

In my work I meet a wide variety of people representing waterway user groups, water companies, environmental regulators, engineering consultants, environmental groups, commercial developers and, most importantly, the public. This diversity of customers and clients means that the job is continually changing.

It is important to plan our water resources for the future and we are just completing strategic water management plans for all 26 of our waterway units. We have also commissioned a world first canal water resources model, which will provide us with a tool to assess our future needs for water and improve our management decisions. The idea that the canal network can be used to transfer water from its source to points where it is needed is not new, but the grander idea of a water grid and a private partner to treat the water is now a reality and this provides not only my team, but the organisation with an exciting opportunity.

The Chartered Institution of Water and Environmental Management (CIWEM) is the preferred route to Chartered status for hydrologists and I was lucky enough to become a Chartered Member in 1998. I have just been invited onto their Water Resources Panel, which is made up of experts across the UK water sector. CIWEM provides my team with the opportunity to reach Chartered status, update their knowledge through Continuing Professional Development (CPD) and through a proposed structured training programme to progress from graduate to full member."

Oda Dijksterhuis - Heritage Lottery Fund Partnership Project Ecologist, Kennet & Avon Canal

"The £29 million restoration of the Kennet & Avon Canal is now nearing the end of its five year programme. Since June 1999 I've been working as the canal's Heritage Lottery Fund (HLF) Partnership Project Ecologist, assessing sites before engineering work begins. I'm responsible for the planning, design and implentation of all ecological aspects of both major and minor engineering works, including canal relining, construction of moorings and byweirs, dredging, installation of bank protection and habitat creation. I'm currently writing a Biodiversity Action Plan (BAP) for the canal.

I've always been interested in aquatic ecology and canals. In fact, I spent much of my childhood on canals and lakes in the Netherlands on my family's sailing barge. After attending agricultural college, I studied for a BSc in Environmental Science in the Netherlands and then gained an MSc at Newcastle University.

Before joining the HLF team I worked in three different jobs with local authority Countryside Teams in the North East of England where I was responsible for many ecological and countryside projects.

I have really enjoyed my role in the HLF project, particularly having the chance to work with a wide range of professionals from different disciplines including engineers, landscape architects and water quality scientists. The design solutions developed through this multi-disciplinary approach have earned our project the 'Engineering in the Natural Environment Award 2002' from the Engineering Council.

After the project is complete I hope to continue working in canal ecology, bringing the knowledge and experience I've gained to new challenges."

Grahame Newman - Policy Co-ordination Manager, Conservation and Regeneration Group, British Waterways

"I graduated in Zoology, and then obtained an MSc in Environmental Pollution Science by part time study. Soon afterwards I joined the Institute of Water Pollution Control, one of CIWEM's predecessors.

Following some years in the water industry, I moved to British Waterways (BW) as Water Quality Scientist in a team providing environmental support to the organisation. As the need for environmental professionals grew, I established and managed a team of water quality specialists.

We advise our engineering, commercial, and operational staff on how to avoid pollution. We also monitor the work of the government's regulators, the Environment Agency and the Scottish Environment Protection Agency, to ensure priorities for water quality improvements reflect our business needs.

A recent reorganisation has given me the opportunity to broaden my experience by joining a newly established Environment Policy team set up to develop policy and strategy for BW. I have a particular responsibility to advise the organisation on the implications of new legislation and government policy.

I have been active in CIWEM for some years, and am now a member of Council and a Fellow. In BW, we consider CIWEM to be a key professional body for environmental staff, and value it as a route for staff to achieve, and then maintain, professional status."

Contacts

Association of Inland Navigation Authorities
Willow Grange, Church Road, Watford, WD17 4QA
Tel: 01642 590257
E-mail: philip.burgess@aina.org.uk
www.aina.org.uk

British Waterways
Willow Grange, Church Road, Watford, WD17 4QA
Tel: 01923 226422 (General) / 01923 201120 (Customer Services)
E-mail: enquiries.hq@britishwaterways.co.uk
www.britishwaterways.co.uk

The Broads Authority
18 Colegate, Norwich, Norfolk, NR3 1BQ
Tel: 01603 610734
E-mail: webenquiries@broads-authority.gov.uk
www.broads-authority.gov.uk

Department of Environment Food and Rural Affairs (DEFRA)
Nobel House, 17 Smith Square, London, SW1P 3JR
Tel: 0207 238 6000

E-mail: helpline@defra.gsi.gov.uk
www.defra.gov.uk

Environment Agency
Rio House, Waterside Drive, Aztec West, Almondsbury, Bristol, BS32 4UD
Tel: 01454 624400
E-mail: enquiries@environment-agency.gov.uk
www.environment-agency.gov.uk

Inland Waterways Amenity Advisory Council
City Road Lock, 38 Graham Street, N1 8JX
Tel: 0207 253 1745
E-mail: iwaac@btinternet.com

Inland Waterways Association
Head Office, PO Box 114, Rickmansworth, WD3 1ZY
Tel: 01923 897000
E-mail: iwa@waterways.org.uk
www.waterways.org.uk

The Waterways Trust
The Trust House, Church Road, Watford, WD17 4QA
Tel: 01923 201494
E-mail: enquiries.hq@thewaterwaystrust.co.uk
www.thewaterwaystrust.co.uk

Magazines

Canal Boat
Waterways World
Canal & Riverboat

References

Department for Transport, Local Government and the Regions (2000) *Waterways for Tomorrow*

13. Flood Defence / Coastal & River Engineering

Ian Hope, Environment Agency

The Sector

Flooding and coastal erosion can have serious consequences for people and their property, and for businesses. It is estimated that about 8% (around 10,000 square kilometres) of the total land area in England is at risk from flooding from rivers, estuaries and the sea. Some 1.8 million properties are identified as being at risk from flooding. If existing flood defences in England and Wales were allowed to fall into disrepair, DEFRA (Department for Environment, Food & Rural Affairs) estimates the consequent annual average economic damage from flooding would be £2 billion. Damage can never be eliminated but our existing defences reduce the annual average value of flood damage to about £400 million.

Coastal defence generally involves many disciplines to predict and manage the evolution of the coastline and estuaries. Flood defence and flood risk management also have a broad discipline base to predict and manage the risk of flooding. The sector also includes other engineering elements: shoreline structures such as outfalls, marinas and piers, dredging and beach recharge industries, and support services such as surveying.

Most work in the UK, and much overseas work, is government or bank funded, and the need for works is subjected to a stringent appraisal process, based on technical, economic and environmental criteria. The nature of the water's edge and its valuable and scarce habitats requires a strong emphasis on sustainability, and links the sector with the environmental impact assessment (EIA) sector (chapter 22).

Flood and coastal modelling, geomorphology, economics and a full range of engineering, managing and operational roles are all essential to the management of river and coastal defence.

Sector Profile

About 4,000 professionals and 2,200 river and land drainage operatives are employed in the sector. The professional sector is growing at about 10% per annum. In 2001, total expenditure by the Environment Agency on inland flood defences was some £244 million. Expenditure on capital projects is set to rise to £173 million per annum in 2002 and significantly thereafter. Coastal defence expenditure is currently about £65 million per annum.

Typical Post Names

Flood Defence Officer, Flood Defence Engineer, River Engineer, Project Manager, Coastal Engineer, Geomorphologist, Flood Warning Officer, Strategic Planning Engineer/Officer, Improvements Engineer/Officer, Economist

Main Employers

The Environment Agency is the largest single authority carrying out flood defence work in England and Wales. The Agency maintains a very limited design capacity and nearly all of its new work is contracted out to engineering consultants and contractors. The Agency also procures strategic analyses of future coastline and river catchment behaviour, usually through consultants.

Local Authorities undertake flood defence and watercourse maintenance on smaller watercourses, and also undertake coastal defence works.

Consultancies are a major employer of a diverse range of staff including engineers, project managers, modellers, economists, and geomorphologists. The consultancy sector is mainly small to medium-sized businesses of 200 to 500 staff, with a few larger organisations. University-based consultancies are also appearing within the sector.

Contractors mainly employ engineering professionals within this sector.

Career Opportunities

The traditional route has been through gaining an engineering qualification (a Degree, HNC, or HND), but increasingly the sector is broadening and different skill sets are useful, particularly good communications and negotiation skills and project management ability. Most new entrants are qualified to a minimum of degree level. Employers generally offer training to join a chartered professional body such as the Chartered Institution of Water and Environmental Management (CIWEM). Graduate starting salaries are around £18,000 for consultants and £24,000 for contractors, rising to £30,000 with experience.

Issues and Trends

Risk Management: It is estimated that some eight per cent (around 10,000 square kilometres) of the total land area in England is at risk from flooding from rivers, tidal rivers and estuaries. 1.8 million properties have been identified as being at risk from flooding. The basis of flood risk management lies in assessing, evaluating and quantifying risk, and establishing long term plans for land use and defence management.

Technology: The exploitation of new technology is beginning to play a more significant role in the management of flood risk. A national programme of flood risk mapping ensures that flood risk information is included in all planning decisions. Technology is enabling new advances in modelling and data management, as well as in communication. Many employers now offer home working, and much consultation is undertaken on the web.

Climate Change and Global Warming: Climate change is probably the single greatest issue being addressed at present. Early research indicates sea level rise and a consquent threat of inundation from the sea. Changes in weather patterns such as heavier and more prolonged rainfall may be likely and could have a marked impact on the sector.

Private Finance Initiative (PFI) and Public Private Partnership (PPP): These are examples of innovative sources of funding which are being used to finance flood defence schemes. Partnering arrangements between clients, consultants and contractors are also becoming more common.

Research and Development (R&D): About £10 million is spent by Government each year on R&D identifying and exploiting developing flood and coastal defence technology, and ensuring future activities are based on good science.

Government, Regional Assemblies and Local Authorities: Flood defence is a high priority political issue, more so now than at any time in the modern era. Society's demand for a flood free environment has to be balanced against costs, and the acceptability of infrequent wide scale flooding is one of the key political questions of the day.

Personal Profiles

Clair Mercer - Flood Warning Officer, Environment Agency

"I would recommend that your first job should give you a range of experience to give you a strong foundation. You need to evaluate the training programme and whether the training leads to professional qualifications. You also need to think about opportunities for personal development that the employer can provide. Skills and qualifications wise, I had a degree in Environmental Science. I also had excellent communication skills (in this job employers want people who can express themselves well). My computer skills were also a tremendous advantage - there is a need for people who really know programs like Access, Excel and Word, for example.

The Environment Agency has a complex structure spanning many functions and interests. Working for the Agency, I learned how a major operating authority actually discharges its functions and delivers its service. The most important thing I learned was never to underestimate the amount of planning and consideration that goes into an action such as delivering a Flood Warning and encouraging someone to act on it. A significant challenge for me was liasing with public interests groups, engaging them, and offering advice and support on flood-related issues. It is a nice feeling knowing that I am doing something for the general good of the public.

In Flood Warning, the responsibility is very real, and during a flood event you appreciate how important effective teamwork is and how your own judgement, combined with the advice of others, influences the quality of decision making. It is very difficult to convey the effort and commitment that is put into flood management until you have experienced it first-hand. I have also really learned the difference between information and knowledge. I learned how to develop a flood warning service from existing data and that I never had enough information. Even with the best available technology some parts of my job were more akin to an art than a science!

Now, my day-to-day responsibilities involve advising members of the public and other operating authorities on a diverse range of Flood Warning issues. I frequently attend meetings with communities to explain the warning process and the measures that the individual can take to minimise the effect of flooding. I have developed my influencing skills and they are incredibly important in my job; it is only through influence and education that we can really make a difference."

Neil Gunn - Area Strategic Planning Engineer, Environment Agency

"I qualified with an HND in Agricultural Engineering and an MSc in Soil and Water Engineering. Apart from these Engineering qualifications and work experience my computer skills were also a big plus - there is a lot of need for people who can use programs like Word and Excel, can use Geographical Information Systems (GIS), and are comfortable working with new technology. I replied to a newspaper advertisement for development control officer with the Environment Agency, and after working in that post for about a year I transferred to the Agency's strategic planning section where I have been for the past 18 months."

Working for the Environment Agency, I have learned how a major Operating Authority actually works, and got a really good insight on how to plan for a 50 year event horizon, the politics that are involved in bringing together the plan and the things that you have to pay attention to that you don't realise at first. On a day-to-day basis I am involved in developing strategic river catchment plans. The Agency is about to draw up strategic plans on a river catchment basis across England and Wales. These plans are needed because changes in climate and rainfall patterns are expected to lead to an increased risk of flooding, and many houses and businesses in this country have been built in flood plains. I run a very sophisticated database based on GIS and I am responsible for making sure that the information it contains is as good as possible. Lots of other people rely on it, and good flood risk information is very important for flood forecasting, warning and protection as it forms the basis of flood risk management. Another aspect of my job is to work with other authorities like local councils who are responsible for flood defence, and to make sure that we all work together."

Anthea Gillham - Senior River Engineer, Arup

"I would recommend a first job with a multi-disciplinary engineering consultancy, with a strong water and environmental section. Look at the type of work they do and ensure they cover a broad range of expertise, then you will be able to move around and find the area of the industry you enjoy the most. If they have a good training programme that includes external courses, and support their staff through further qualifications, this is highly beneficial. Make sure the company mentors their graduates through structured training schemes to help them achieve professional qualifications, such as Incorporated or Chartered Engineer status.

I qualified with a degree in Civil Engineering and an MSc in Hydrology and Environmental Management. I applied for my first job as a graduate through an advert placed in New Civil Engineer. Arup have a graduate recruitment system, for which you can apply through their head office in London. If you are successful in the first stage, you then meet the staff in the office where you would be placed, which depends on the type of work you would like to do. Alternatively, you can write direct to the sector you would like to work in.

From the start I worked on a wide range of projects, from feasibility studies to hydraulic modelling and civil engineering design. I gained experience in all aspects of the water industry, including environmental appraisals, water treatment, river engineering and hydrology. This helped me to specialise in an area which I really enjoy. The structured training system has ensured my training needs are always met and I am encouraged to undertake courses that help my job. I recently gained my Chartered Engineer (CEng) qualification, which reflected the diverse work I have undertaken.

In a job such as mine, you are expected to be responsible for your work from an early stage. You are given plenty of opportunities to show your ability and encouraged to take responsibility for projects on a technical and project management level quite early in your career. The workload is usually high, but the projects you get involved with are very interesting. I am currently responsible for delivering the design for two major flood alleviation schemes which the Environment Agency are funding. I work closely with the Contractor to develop sustainable designs and ensure they are constructed in time and to budget.

Most river engineering and flood defence design work is now undertaken by engineering consultancies, so since joining Arup I have been involved in a number of schemes. I have undertaken hydraulic modelling of river systems to determine the erosion risk. I have produced feasibility studies for river enhancement and restoration schemes and I have also worked on schemes for private clients, such as developers and councils, where they are looking to develop near river corridors and require our flood risk and management services."

Dr Richard Crowder - Halcrow

"I specialise in flood risk assessments and the modelling of flood alleviation schemes, flood warning scheme development, water resource problems and water quality risk assessments. As a consulting engineer my workload is varied, and at times unpredictable. We supply a direct service to clients as well as supporting other divisions in project delivery.

With respect to flood risk assessments we are often assessing the risk of flooding at a particular site. We then may have to work with our engineering division to develop mitigation measures and then prove them.

On route to my current job I initially undertook a Civil and Structural Engineering Degree and was fortunate enough to be offered a research position on an EC funded Research and Development (R&D) project based in Holland. I then became a Research Assistant on an Environment Agency funded R&D project in the UK. I then took the full time role of senior modeller and then subsequently divisional manager with Bullen Consultants. For some reason I decided to study part time for a PhD, which has certainly paid off for me in the long run.

I became a Full Member of the Chartered Institution of Water and Environmental Management and now sit on the local branch committee. Not only does this help me to keep abreast of events and activities in the area of environmental management but is also keeps me in touch with friends and professionals in the industry who work for other organisations."

Ian Hope - Head of Flood Defence Policy & Process, Environment Agency

"Flood defence is a high priority issue, probably more so now than at any time in recent years. There can be few jobs where the changes have been so radical and in such a short period of time. From an established and well-understood role of Flood Defence we have moved away from pure defence and are much more focussed on flood risk management with fully integrated planning. This change in focus means that not only do we take a different approach but it has also meant helping the people in the business adjust to this new way of doing things.

I have worked in flood defence for 4 years, initially as an Area Flood Defence Manager, then in a Regional role which included responsibilities for a range of professional disciplines. Now I play a national role, as Head of Flood Defence Policy & Process.

I joined the Environment Agency from a background in engineering, contracting and consulting and before that I worked for a water company. In looking back all of my jobs have been interesting and rewarding and have prepared me for the role I find myself in now. Apart from the engineering qualifications, which accompanied my early career, I found that I increasingly needed to develop my understanding of wider management skills as a discipline, as well as practising it as an art. This has meant that I have never been less than a year from exposure to some form of higher education or management orientated CPD.

Policy and Process is about future scanning; determining what we are likely to be doing in the future so that we can plan now to meet the priorities and demands of the 21st century, together with ensuring that we adopt a consistent approach across the country. Due to the size of the job, you have to operate very close to your limits. This means having to delegate and, importantly, trust people to deliver together with mastering complex briefs quickly.

On a day to day basis, I make sure that the Agency has the right plans, policies and processes in place. To do this I am leading a team that is planning now for the future. This means being able to predict the manpower needs for next year and successive years, planning for succession into key roles, planning the Agency's recruitment, liasing with personnel specialists to put the plans into practice and influencing universities to develop courses that provide the skills that the Agency needs."

Contacts

Association of Drainage Authorities
The Mews , Royal Oak Passage, Huntingdon, Cambridgesire, PE18 6EA
Tel : 01480 411123
www.ada.org.uk/flooddefence

Department for Environment Food & Rural Affairs
Nobel House, 17 Smith Square, London SW1P 3JR
Tel: 020 7238 6000
www.defra.gov.uk/environ/fcd/default.htm

Environment Agency
Rio House, Waterside Drive, Aztec West, Almonsbury, Bristol, BS32 4UD
Tel: 01454 624400
www.environment-agency.gov.uk/subjects/flood

National Assembly for Wales
Cardiff Bay, Cardiff CF99 1NA
Tel: 029 20 825111
www.wales.gov.uk

Northern Ireland Department of Agriculture and Rural Development
Dundonald House, Upper Newtownards Road, Belfast BT4 3SB
Tel: (028) 90524999
www.northernireland.gov.uk

Principal Engineering Consultants

Babtie Group
Simpson House, 6 Cherry Orchard Road, CROYDON, Surrey CR9 6BE
www.babtie.co.uk

Binnie Black & Veatch,Grosvenor House, 69 London Road,
Redhill, Surrey RH1 1LQ
www.bbv-ltd.com

Halcrow Group
Peterscourt, City Road, Peterborough PE1 1SA
www.halcrow.co.uk

HR Wallingford Ltd
Howbery Park, Wallingford, Oxfordshire, OX10 8BA
Tel: 01491 835381
www.hrwallingford.co.uk

W S Atkins
Woodcote Grove, Ashley Road, Epsom, Surrey, KT18 5BW
www.atkinsglobal.com

Principal Engineering Contractors

Alfred McAlpine Civil Engineering
West Carr Road, Retford, Nottinghamshire DN22 7SW
www.alfred-mcalpine.com

Edmund Nuttall Ltd
1 Eagle House, Asama Court, Newcastle Business Park, Newcastle-upon-Tyne
NE4 7LN
www.edmund-nuttall.co.uk

Harbour & General
Springwell Road, Springwell, Gateshead, Tyne & Wear NE9 5SP

J. Breheny Contractors Ltd
Flordon Road, Creeting St Mary, Ipswich, Suffolk IP6 8NH
www.breheny.co.uk

Jackson Civil Engineering a Division of Certas Plc.
Jackson House, 84 Sandyhill Lane, Ipswich, Suffolk IP3 0NA
www.jackson-civils.co.uk

Mowlem Civil Engineering
Foundation House, Eastern Road, Bracknell, Berkshire RG12 2UZ
www.mowlem.co.uk

Van Oord ACZ Ltd
Lockside Place, Mill Lane, Newbury, Berkshire RG14 5QS
www.voacz.com/en/index

Useful Contacts

Chartered Institution of Water and Environmental Management (CIWEM)
15 John Street, London WC1N 2EB
Tel: 020 7831 3110
www.ciwem.com

Institution of Civil Engineers,
1, Great George Street, Westminster, London, SW1P 3AA
Tel: 020 7 222 7722
www.ice.org.uk

Specialist Contacts

Flood Hazard Research Centre
Middlesex University
www.fhrc.mdx.ac.uk/contents.html

UK Climate Impacts Programme
www.ukcip.org.uk

UK Local Government information
www.gwydir.demon.co.uk/uklocalgov

Water Environment Research Foundation (WERF)
Manages research on watershed management.
E-mail: werf@werf.org

14. Water Resources Management

Glenn Watts, Environment Agency

The Sector

Water resources management ensures that reliable water supplies can be maintained in a way that meets human needs while protecting the environment. A clean, reliable water supply is vital for human health and also contributes to economic development through its use in commerce, industry and agriculture. While the UK is often considered to have a wet climate, our high population density and valuable natural environment means that there are conflicting demands for water.

Water resources management considers both the availability of water and how it is used. It involves understanding how much water is in rivers and groundwater and how this needs to be managed to protect the environment. Water resources managers need to understand present and future demand for water, and to consider options for meeting this - ranging from developing new resources such as reservoirs to managing demand through technological and behavioural change.

Water resources managers must combine an understanding of human behaviour with environmental science. It's a challenging but rewarding career, demanding clear thinking, an ability to understand different views and an ability to find innovative solutions that meet the needs of society and protect the environment now and for the future.

Sector Profile

The sector employs around 1500 people in the UK, mainly in government agencies, water companies and environmental and engineering consultancies. While numbers employed in water companies are fairly stable, there is slow growth in the public sector and in consultancy.

Typical Post Names

Water Resources Planner, Water Resources Engineer, Abstraction Licensing Officer, Demand Forecaster, Water Resources Analyst, Water Resources Economist, Hydrologist, Hydrogeologist, Hydroecologist

Main Employers

Environment Agency, Scottish Environment Protection Agency (SEPA), Water Companies, Ofwat (Office of Water Services), Engineering Consultancies

Career Opportunities

Most new entrants are graduates in a numerate discipline - typically geography, environmental science, engineering or economics - but there are increasing opportunities for social scientists. Many people also hold higher degrees, such as MScs in water resources or engineering hydrology.

Public Sector
In England and Wales, the Environment Agency is the main public sector employer. With around 600 water resources staff, there is a wide variety of different opportunities. Abstraction licensing officers deal with applications to take water from rivers or groundwater. They have to understand the needs of the applicant and decide whether their proposals are environmentally acceptable and do not affect other water users. Water resources planners take a long-term view, looking at future needs for water and the ways that these can be met. Hydrologists and hydrogeologists provide technical analysis to support decision-making on licence decisions and water resources strategies. Hydrologists may also be involved in flood warning and forecasting, while hydrogeologists often cover groundwater quality issues as well.

In Scotland the Scottish Environment Protection Agency (SEPA) carries out many of these roles, and in Northern Ireland DARD (Department of Agriculture and Rural Development) and DOE(NI) (Department of the Environment in Northern Ireland) take responsibility for these issues. Ofwat also employs water resources economists to look at supply-demand balance, leakage and water efficiency issues. Public sector starting salaries for new graduates or inexperienced MScs are £15,000 to £18,000. Typically this would rise to between £22,000 and £28,000 with 5 to 10 years' experience.

Private Sector
In England and Wales, water companies are one of the main employers in the private sector, with around 400 water resources staff in total. Water resources analysts identify future demand and make returns to Ofwat about how water has been used. Water resources planners consider options for meeting future demand and implement these options. Considerable negotiation with regulators and pressure groups may be needed, and innovative solutions are often required. Where resource development is needed, water resources engineers need to develop detailed plans. Leakage engineers understand, track and manage the leakage of water from the mains network, while water companies also need hydrologists and hydrogeologists to understand how rivers and aquifers work and ensure that water supplies will continue to be secure. Typical starting salaries for new graduates are £18,000 to £20,000. With 5 to 10 years' experience this would rise to between £25,000 and £35,000.

Consultancies constitute another important private sector employer, with about 400 people employed in water resources. Consultants support all of the activities of the public sector and water companies, with some offering particular scarce skills. The variety of work can be challenging and consultants need to be adaptable. Project management skills are vital, and consultants often need to meet strict deadlines and budgets. Many consultants in the water resources field also apply their knowledge overseas. Typically, consultants require strong numerical and scientific backgrounds. Starting salaries for new graduates are £18,000 to £20,000. With 5 to 10 years experience this would rise to £25,000 to £35,000.

Non-Profit Sector
There are few non-profit organisations that specifically employ water resources experts, though the Royal Society for the Protection of Birds and the Wildlife Trusts do employ a small number. An ability to understand the full range of issues is vital. Starting salaries are similar to those in the public sector.

Issues and Trends

Water resources are under increasing pressure. Population growth, the trend towards smaller households, increased affluence and different water use habits may make water use grow in some areas, particularly in the dry south and east. Industrial demand for water is falling, reflecting both a change in the industrial base and increased efficiency in industrial processes. On the other hand, people expect enhanced protection of the natural environment, and new European regulations such as the Habitats Directive and the Water Framework Directive will mean that some water company abstractions have to be modified.

In much of southern England there is little new water available for abstraction. Meeting future demands will require innovative approaches to using present supplies as effectively as possible, managing demand, and finding new sources of water. Collaborative approaches will become increasingly important, and negotiating skills may be as important as technical knowledge. The Government is proposing to extend competition in the water industry and has consulted on new water resources legislation. This is a fascinating time to be involved in water resources management.

Personal Profiles

Emma Blunden - Water Resources Planner, Environment Agency

"I work as a Water Resources Planner for the Environment Agency at the Bristol Head Office. The purpose of my job is to provide technical and specialist expertise. We provide the national focus for long-term planning to develop water resources policies, procedures and plans. This covers many interesting aspects of water resources management from assessing water companies' plans to supply public water to understanding how much water we all use each day.

I've been working in the water industry/environmental consultancy for over seven years. I graduated from Leeds University with a BSc in Geography. As I enjoyed the hydrology aspects of the course I decided to study for a Masters in Water Resources Technology and Management at Birmingham University.

After completing my MSc at Birmingham, I started work as an Engineering Hydrologist for ADAS (a consultancy and research body). This involved hydraulic modelling and design of storage ponds for run-off from open cast sites, running small projects for environmental assessments, site assessments and surveys. After a year at ADAS I moved to Southern Water as an Engineering Hydrologist. I was working at Southern Water during the 1997 drought so a lot of my work focused on drought projects requiring the analysis of hydrological information and hydraulic modelling. I also worked on estimation of surface water source yields. After a couple of years at Southern Water I moved to Halcrow Engineering Consultants in Swindon. At Halcrow I worked on a variety of projects as part of a team providing hydrological, water resources planning and hydraulic modelling expertise. My time at Halcrow provided me with a wide range of skills. I left Halcrow to work for the Environment Agency in 1999."

Dr Ed Smith - Water Strategy Manager, Anglian Water Services

"I work for Anglian Water Services which provides water supplies and the treatment of wastewater for homes and businesses in East Anglia. It has the largest geographical area of supply of the water companies and covers one of the highest growth regions in England.

My job is to help the company to provide water to homes and businesses and to make sure we invest money in pumps, pipes and new water resources in time to satisfy existing demands and to plan for future growth. This requires evaluation of the reliability of our water supplies, which come from rivers, reservoirs and boreholes drilled to tap underground water. In planning for the future we must make sure we can supply water during droughts and take into account the impact of climate change. We must do all of this without any significant impact on the water environment. My job also includes helping to manage existing demands for water. We do this by ensuring leaks from our 36,000km of water mains remain low, installing water meters to new homes and to customers who request them and advising customers on how to avoid wasting water through advice both personally and on our website.

My interest in water started when I was at university, where I studied geology and physics and undertook a PhD in hydrogeology. This involved understanding how water flows in rocks underground and how you could abstract the water for water supply. My first job was for a water authority where I was responsible for investigating an underground water body (known as an aquifer) for future supplies to the city of Peterborough. This involved managing contracts to drill boreholes and building a mathematical model of the aquifer so we could calculate how best to manage it.

My career has developed into a more managerial role, which has included producing abstraction licences, which give permissions to abstract water, water resources plans for government scrutiny and helping to manage water supplies during droughts. I now work on a number of national groups which review policy and regulations. Basically this involves looking at the way we manage water supplies to ensure they give value to customers and minimise impacts on the environment. I have found my job most rewarding as water is essential for life. Because of the good quality and reliability of water in the UK, we thankfully live in a society that doesn't have to concern itself with these issues as, unfortunately, many other countries have to."

Ben Piper - Associate, Atkins Water

"I am an Associate with Atkins Water and work from the Oxford office. The purpose of my job is to procure, manage and conduct projects concerned with water resource planning and, increasingly, the environmental consequences of the way in which we make use of the water environment and how this should be better managed in the future.

From a first degree in Mechanical Sciences and an MSc in Pollution and Environmental Control, I joined the then Institute of Hydrology in Wallingford. My work included extensive periods of fieldwork, hydrological analysis and numerical modelling. As part of a Government funded Research Institute, I also began to work on the provision of policy and strategic advice to Government Departments. I was given the opportunity to work overseas in 1975, and then spent the next 15 years working on water resource and irrigation projects overseas.

Mid-career I decided to leave Wallingford and move to General Utilities Projects - the UK Engineering Consultancy of the Compagnie Générale des Eaux. On behalf of the four water-only companies in the Group, I was responsible for providing technical inputs on water resource planning for regulatory submissions to the Environment Agency and OFWAT. In addition to quantitative water balances, the work also required economic analysis. I continued to be involved in providing policy and strategic advice and worked on the Project Steering Group of various research projects funded by UK Water Industry Research (UKWIR). I was also involved on the fringe of operational aspects of water supply, giving technical advice during emergency incidents. I was a member of the Managing Director's Drought Management Committee that met every Friday morning to plan and manage the response to the steadily evolving drought of 1997-1998.

Now at Atkins I continue to be involved with water resource planning, working for both water companies and for the Environment Agency. Of increasing importance in this work is the need to consider not only water quantity, but also water quality and the environmental consequences of abstractions, discharges and land-use policy. Understanding and quantifying uncertainties such as the potential impact of climate change on demands and supplies is also an important part of my work."

Contacts

British Hydrological Society (BHS)
www.hydrology.org.uk

The British Hydrological Society has the aim of promoting interest and scholarship in both the scientific and applied aspects of hydrology. It pursues these aims by holding major national and international symposiums as well as regular technical meetings in a variety of locations around the country, circulating a lively quarterly newsletter, publishing occasional papers, and building links with other national and international organisations with shared interests. BHS aims to keep members abreast of new developments in hydrology and to provide a forum for sharing knowledge and experience.

The Society works with professional bodies, including CIWEM, to ensure that they recognise the needs of BHS members and are able to provide a route to professional membership for hydrologists. Membership costs are low and BHS encourages active participation. Some activities are specifically targeted at student members, and career development.

The Chartered Institution of Water and Environmental Management (CIWEM)
www.ciwem.org.uk

Department for Environment, Food & Rural Affairs (DEFRA)
www.defra.gov.uk/environment/water/index.htm#Resources

Drinking Water Inspectorate
www.dwi.gov.uk

Environment Agency - water resources
www.environment-agency.gov.uk/subjects/waterres/?lang=_e

Environment and Heritage Service, Northern Ireland
Tel: 028 9025 4758
www.ehsni.gov.uk

National Water Demand Management Centre
www.environment-agency.gov.uk/Savewater

Office of Water Services (Ofwat)
www.ofwat.gov.uk

Scottish Environment Protection Agency (SEPA)
www.sepa.org.uk

Water UK - umbrella organisation for water companies in the UK, with
addresses, contact details and links
www.water.org.uk

15. Drinking Water Quality & Wastewater Management

Graham Cleverly, Independent Water & Environmental Consultant

The Sector

Historical perspective: The abstraction, safe treatment and distribution of drinking water to the customer's tap and the collection, treatment and safe disposal of wastewater continue to make a vital contribution to public health throughout the world. However, until the middle of the19th Century, water and sanitation provision was rudimentary or non-existent in most industrialised cities in the world including those in the UK, for all but the very wealthy. Water-borne diseases such as typhoid and cholera were widespread and were responsible for countless deaths particularly amongst children. Life expectancy for most people in Britain was no more than around 35 years. No-one was immune from the public health dangers of drinking contaminated water; Queen Victoria's husband Prince Albert died from typhoid fever in 1861.

There has always been a close link between the provision of drinking water and wastewater services. This chapter therefore looks at them together. A celebrated incident investigated by Dr John Snow in Broad Street, London in 1854 concerning a public hand pump, demonstrated for the first time the link between pollution from sewage and the occurrence of cholera. By removing the pump handle from the contaminated drinking water supply he immediately stopped the source of the pollution. This incident (the beginning of the science of epidemiology) and work by other earlier Reformers including Sir Edward Chadwick were instrumental in the major improvements in water and sanitation facilities for London and other major cities in Europe and North America which continue to this day. Life expectancy in most developed countries is now double the figure in 1850 with improved water and sanitation services being the biggest contributing public health factor.

European Environmental Directives: The biggest factor driving environmental investments in the UK in the last few years has been the implementation of the Urban Wastewater Directive which came into force in 1990. This Directive sets high standards for discharges from wastewater plants and requires significant new investments in secondary treatment at most wastewater treatment works together with the cessation of all sludge dumping to sea. Other drivers for investment have been:
·   the Drinking Water Directives (which set out quality standards for a range of microbiological, chemical and indicator parameters and have driven similar large investments in both new and upgraded water treatment plants and water distribution networks);
·   the Bathing Water Directive (which sets water quality standards for bathing waters and has driven large investments in wastewater treatment); and
·   the Nitrates Directive (which limits the application of fertilisers to nitrate sensitive zones to prevent damage to human health and eutrophication of surface waters).

Recent improvements in water and wastewater quality in England and Wales:
·   The Drinking Water Inspectorate's 12th Annual Report for 2001 shows that 99.83% of the 2.7 million drinking water samples taken (and covering a long

list of microbiological, chemical and taste parameters) met the required standards.

· The Environment Agency's figures for pollution incidents show a reduction in wastewater effluent discharge incidents for 1999 and 2000 compared with 1998 and an improvement in the number of beaches achieving the Bathing Water Directive standards in 2001.

Scotland: Results in Scotland are also showing improvements in the quality of drinking water, bathing water and wastewater effluent.

Privatisation: In England and Wales, the water and wastewater industry was privatised in 1989 and huge investments have been made and will continue for the next few years in order to achieve the necessary improvements in drinking water and wastewater services to customers. There are currently 10 large Regional Water Companies providing water and wastewater services in England and Wales and 14 smaller Companies supplying only water services. Between 1989 and 2000, new capital investment in the water industry amounted to about £35billion, with about 50% related to environmental and water quality improvements.

Regulation in England and Wales: In England and Wales the Privatised Water Companies are regulated by a number of government agencies each with a specific responsibility:

· *The Drinking Water Inspectorate* (DWI) is the drinking water quality regulator and is responsible for checking that the water companies in England and Wales supply water at the tap that is safe to drink and meets the standards set in the latest Water Supply (Water Quality) Regulations.

· *OFWAT* (the Office of Water Services) is the economic regulator and is responsible for making sure that the water and sewage companies in England and Wales give customers a good-quality, efficient service at a fair price.

· *The Environment Agency* is the principal Regulator for environmental performance and is responsible amongst other environmental responsibilities for licensing, monitoring and enforcing effluent discharge standards to receiving waters from wastewater treatment plants. This pollution control activity is more fully described in Chapter 17 on Water Qualty & Pollution Control".

Regulation in Scotland: In Scotland, environmental water quality regulation is the responsibility of the Scottish Environment Protection Agency (SEPA) and drinking water quality regulation is undertaken by the Drinking Water Quality Regulator. Economic regulation and protection of customer services is undertaken by the Water Industry Commissioner for Scotland.

The Developing World: In most developing countries the water and sanitation situation is a different picture altogether with an estimated 2.4 billion people without access to adequate sanitation. A recent report from Tearfund and Wateraid, two leading British Development Agencies, indicates that twenty million children will die in the developing word in the next 10 years unless governments take urgent action to address preventable diseases caused by inadequate sanitation.

Key Issues in the UK

Some key issues in the provision and management of water and wastewater services in the UK are:

· Continuing to provide high quality water and wastewater services. This is in the face of increasing competition (in England and Wales), and increasing customer expectations across the UK

· Achieving the very large UK investment programme between now and 2005/6

· Maintaining strict trade effluent control

· Ensuring that drinking water quality and wastewater effluent quality standards are maintained at the works

· Undertaking rehabilitation of water networks through addressing issues including lead and iron removal and prevention of cryptosporidiosis to ensure the quality of water at the tap complies with required standards

· Undertaking rehabilitation and upgrading of sewerage networks to reduce flooding

· Upgrading of emergency storm overflows to improve river quality

Sector profile

A wide range of people work in drinking water and wastewater management, including:

· Water treatment and wastewater treatment plant operations staff working to achieve and maintain the standards required at the works (Water Companies)

· Water distribution and sewerage network engineers working to ensure that the sewage and water distribution networks are designed, operated and maintained to standard.

· Water and Wastewater (sometimes called Public Health) Consultants who provide a professional service to the Water Companies and the Regulators across a wide range of engineering, economic, financial, health and safety, and environmental issues. These services include feasibility studies, audits, design and construction, supervision and commissioning of new and upgraded works and networks.

· Analytical chemists - responsible for ensuring effective laboratory services

· Specialist laboratory based scientists e.g. chemists, microbiologists, biologists

· Laboratory and field technicians responsible for sampling and analysing water and wastewater samples (Water Companies and private laboratories)

· Process scientists

· Researchers, business environment advisors, Non-Governmental Organisations (NGOs) and pressure groups, local and central Government

· Regulators, who are responsible for monitoring the provision of services by the water companies at a fair price, monitoring the quality of the drinking water at the tap and for monitoring the quality of wastewater effluent discharges to receiving waters.

Typical Post Names

Wastewater Treatment Plant Manager, Water Treatment Plant Manager, Water Engineer, Process Scientist, Environmental Scientist, Environment Protection Officer, Analytical Chemist, Microbiologist, Biologist, Technician, Drinking Water Inspector

Main Employers

The main employers for water and wastewater management activities in the UK are Water Companies and consultancies dealing with public health and engineering. Other relevant organisations with posts in drinking water and wastewater management activities include:

- Industry (mainly industrial treatment operation)
- Office of Water Services (OFWAT)
- Environment Agency
- The Scottish Environment Protection Agency (SEPA)
- The Environment and Heritage Service of the Northern Ireland Department of the Environment
- Drinking Water Inspectorate
- Ministry of Defence (water and wastewater activities: soon to be 'privatised')
- Universities/commercial research bodies e.g. Water Research Centre (WRc)
- Department for International Development (DfID)

Career Opportunities

Water Companies: The Privatised Water Companies in England and Wales together employ over 30,000 staff. For example, United Utilities (UU), who operate over an area of 14,000 square kilometres in north west England and serve 7 million customers, employ 4,100 people. Typical starting salaries for graduates with UU are approximately £18,000 per annum. Modern apprentices start at about £6,000 for those with good GCSEs and £8,000 with 'A' levels, with salaries up to £13,000 on achieving BTEC and £15,000 when fully licensed.

Consultancies: There are a number of large and small specialist consultancies working in the field of drinking water and wastewater management. A typical graduate starting salary with a large engineering consultancy could be £17,500 for an Honours degree, £18,000 for an M.Eng and £18,500 for an Honours degree plus Masters.

Laboratory Scientists: A typical graduate chemist or microbiologist starting salary is from £16,500 and a laboratory technician starting salary is from £11,500.

Issues and Trends

Sustainability: Much of the recent UK environmental legislation including drinking water and wastewater management has been driven by European Directives which embrace sustainability and the precautionary and 'polluter pays' principles. Detailed Directives are in place covering drinking water and urban wastewater management with considerable investment carried out by the water Industry as a result since 1989.

In England and Wales, the next few years will see further investments under the third and fourth Asset Management Plans (AMPs) in the 5 year periods 2001-2005 (AMP3) and 2005-2009 (AMP4). A further £5 billion is to be spent during the period 2000-2005 on further environmental improvements with 70% allocated to alleviating continuous and intermittent sewage discharges and 20% allocated to improvements in the treatment and disposal of sewage sludge.

In Scotland (and also in Northern Ireland) the water and wastewater services remain in public ownership but with increasing private sector investment in improved wastewater services through the Private Finance Initiative (PFI). Scottish Water replaced the three Regional Water Authorities in April 2002 and the planned capital expenditure ("Capex") for the period 2000-2005 is £1.8 billion, most of which is for drinking water improvements, urban wastewater treatment improvements, bathing water improvements and infrastructure improvements for both sewerage and water distribution networks.

Future challenges in the UK: Alongside the routine (but essential) provision of drinking water and wastewater services, future challenges in the UK are likely to include:
- Dealing with competition issues in England and Wales including 'common carriage'
- Introducing new water and wastewater technology including membrane technology
- Dealing with the requirements of new Directives including the Water Framework Directive, the forthcoming revisions to the Bathing Water Directive and the Sewage Sludge to Land Directive.
- Dealing with new drinking water quality issues including endocrine disruptors
- Dealing with diffuse pollution from agriculture and industry

Future challenges overseas: The huge challenge of delivering clean drinking water and sanitation to the world's expanding urban and rural populations is increasingly focussing on new forms of private-public partnerships to improve management and operations, ways of involving NGOs to target those most in need, and ways to improve water demand management including better leakage control.

Opportunities to work overseas in developing countries with voluntary organisations e.g. Voluntary Service Overseas (VSO) as well as consultancies and Aid organisations will continue to grow for practitioners with some experience in both private and public sectors. Enlargement of the European Union is also providing limited opportunities for experienced consultants and seconded staff from regulatory bodies to assist transition countries in Central and Eastern Europe in implementing and applying European Environmental Directives. These include key water Directives such as the Water Framework Directive, the Urban Wastewater Directive, the Integrated Pollution Prevention and Control (IPPC) Directive and the Nitrates Directive.

Personal Profiles

Norman Davies - United Utilities

"I was one of 24 Modern Apprentices appointed from over 1100 applicants by United Utilities (UU) in the first year of an Operations Apprenticeship scheme. The scheme was initiated to counteract the forecasted shortfall of employees in the operations of UU (then Northwest Water) due to retirement and promotion. The first two years consisted of gaining NVQ Level 2 Qualifications in engineering, then getting involved in different parts of the business operations. My experience was gained in Water Management, Customer Operations and then in Waste Water Operations. During this time I attended Manchester Metropolitan University where I gained an HNC in Business Studies, which highlighted various skills I adopted for my own working environment. I am hoping to further my Business qualification to degree level in the next few years, via the Open University.

Upon completion of the scheduled placements, I was selected for Wastewater Operations and continued to work with the Process Controllers at Salford Wastewater Treatment Works (WwTW). Through the apprenticeship scheme I applied for and obtained a role on one of UU's first sludge dryers utilising new technology in November 2000. The dryer was introduced to help UU adhere to new environmental legislation, whilst reducing the costs of sludge disposal due to improving its classification and reducing its quantity. Due to the intensity of the training, I had to postpone my BTEC until further notice, and am now due to complete it in July 2002.

In June 2001 I moved on to Blackburn WwTW, to assist an investigation into compliance problems. The treatment works consists of multiple contributing processes and all needed to be understood to help tackle the problems. I also performed controlled tests and organised the installation and monitoring of a trial unit to aid compliance. I was recently placed at Darwen/Belmont WwTW, and also retain responsibilities at Blackburn WwTW where I will be gaining most of the experience for the WAMITAB (Waste Management Industry Training and Advisory Board) accreditation I started in April 2002."

Rob Flitter - Project Engineer/Manager, Binnie Black & Veatch

"I joined the Chester office of Binnie Black and Veatch in August 1999, with 9 years of varied experience in the Construction Industry. I have, however, always maintained a preference for water-based work.

As part of my degree course at the University of Bradford, I completed a very enjoyable and valuable placement year with Yorkshire Water Engineering Service. Here I assisted in the design and tender document preparation for several water supply schemes. I also gained 3 months site experience on the construction of a reinforced concrete reservoir. It was also a valuable opportunity to pay off some of the accumulating debts from the first two years of study!

Prior to graduation I managed to secure a post with Morrison Construction (then Morrison Shand). During my 5 years with Morrison, I was lucky to work on very varied projects. Initially I was responsible for keeping site records and setting out for projects including a £420,000 reinforced concrete coal reclamation hopper, a £801,000 drainage scheme and a £7.5 million, 5.2km long by-pass. Later in my career I had increasing responsibilities including quality assurance, material requisition and co-ordination of safety on site on a variety of schemes, including a £500,000 industrial unit, road projects valued up to £1 million and demolition.

In order to pursue chartered status I successfully sought a design secondment in 1996, within the Mold design office of Acer Consultants, where I gained valuable design experience in water supply. I was employed on a variety of raw water supply schemes, valued between £100,000 and £250,000, with tasks including carrying out tender design and document preparation, and client and statutory body liaison. Following completion of this 12-month period I was offered a permanent position with Acer, now Hyder Consulting. I was appointed as Lead Design Engineer, on a variety of water and wastewater projects with values of between £30,000 and £40M. Later, I was given project management responsibility for the reinforced concrete and pipework design of a £10M wastewater treatment works and the design of sewer diversions for a £100M road scheme.

Five reasons to join CIWEM

1 We have a global membership of environmental professionals working in all sectors

2 We hold over 250 conferences and events each year attracting around 30,000 delegates

3 Each year we respond to over 40 major consultation documents and publish ten Policy Position Statements and 20 Fact Sheets on key environmental issues

4 We have a global network of Branches and Specialist Interest Groups

5 Our publications, including a highly respected refereed Journal and monthly magazine, are read by over 80,000 people and have a global readership

CIWEM

CIWEM • 15 JOHN STREET • LONDON • WC1N 2EB • TEL: 020 7831 3110 • FAX: 020 7831 2830 • WEB: www.ciwem.org.uk

I then joined Binnie Black & Veatch as Project Engineer/Project Manager. My duties have included project management of £620,000 of Section 105 Flood Risk Studies as well as the design of a £150,000 Environment Agency gauging station in Cheshire and of a £1M canal diversion for British Waterways in the Pennines. More recently I have acted as Project Engineer/Manager providing tender assistance to contractors on design and construct water and wastewater projects, ranging in value from £2.6M to £24M. On several of these projects I was able to continue my involvement into the detail design stage, when the team I was working in successfully won the project.

I am currently awaiting the results of my Chartered Professional Review for the Institution of Civil Engineers and I hope to become a full member of the Chartered Institution of Water and Environmental Management (CIWEM) in the near future.

A typical day in my job might go like this:

…Following a pleasant 20 minute stroll along the canal with a couple of work mates, I arrive in the office at about 8:00. The usual suspects are in early to make the most of the time, before the phone starts ringing. I spend my first half-hour or so with a cuppa, arranging my work for the day and sifting through the e-mails which arrived late yesterday afternoon. The majority of my morning is spent sketching some layouts for our latest tender assistance job. This particular scheme is for £7.6million of improvements to a Water Treatment Works (WTW), constructed in the 1920s. The works operates at an average outlet of 80Ml/day.

The project is to consist of the following main units:

·   A new Inlet Pumping Station to transfer raw water from the raw water reservoir to the new Clarifier.
·   A Clarifier Unit designed to take the full maximum flow of the works of 105Ml/day.
·   Washwater system improvements, including flocculation, clarification and sludge storage.

I am working within a team, preparing the tender submission for this project. My role is to co-ordinate civil and structural elements of the tender design, providing our contractor client with sufficient, timely information in order to provide a compliant bid, whilst constantly looking to provide value engineered solutions. I am also responsible for overseeing the production of tender submission drawings. This is what the sketches I am producing this morning are part of.

As lead civil engineer for this tender design I am managing the geotechnical review and outline civil design. I am also working closely with our internal Hydraulic, Process, Mechanical and Electrical Engineers as well as the partner companies within the team. I am liasing closely with the process contractor on the design of the clarifiers in particular.

It is our main duty to provide the civil quantities for all structures for pricing. My other duties include the internal monitoring of costs for the project and management of Quality Assurance (QA) systems. We are one of four teams invited to submit a tender.

After a brief explanation of what I have tried to draw, I hand my sketches to our Computer Aided Design (CAD) technician for drafting. And after a brief trip to the sandwich shop I return to the office. I reply to a phone message from a potential new client. This contact may provide a different kind of work.

Having been flooded during the downpours of October 2000, a local farmer has put in an insurance claim for damage to his property and feels that the blame lies with the Highways Agency or Highways Department of the council for inadequate drainage maintenance. He wants Binnie Black & Veatch to put a factual report together to support his claim. I arrange to visit his farm early next week.

I then head off, with a colleague, to a Section 105 progress meeting in Warrington. Section 105 of the Water Resources Act, 1991, along with DoE/MAFF Circular 30/92 'Development and Flood Risk' placed a requirement on the National Rivers Authority (NRA) to provide information regarding the extent of flood plains to local Authorities and developers, in order to steer development away from areas under risk of flooding. The resulting flood maps are accessible through the Environment Agency's website and are currently being updated.

In July 1999, Binnie Black & Veatch were invited to submit a proposal for the Middle and Lower Mersey Commission, which was submitted in August, the week I joined the company. Having previously been consulted, I was put forward to the Agency as Project Engineer.

The day-to-day management of the commission is my responsibility. I am responsible for liaison with the client and timely completion of the project within the agreed budget. My duties included the co-ordination of staff resources for hydrological, hydraulic and mapping functions. I was also responsible for the monthly progress reporting to both the client and to the Binnie Black & Veatch internal system.

The challenges faced to-date on this project have included a survey contractor going bankrupt and the catastrophic Foot and Mouth crisis, with all site surveys been halted. Currently the project is over 12 months delayed as a result. The whole team have worked together to get this commission back on the right track. This team attitude is reflected in the progress meeting, where we have built a very good, open relationship with the Agency staff.

Arriving back in the office, I read the e-mail arriving in the afternoon, check on my tender WTW drawing progress, before writing up the minutes from today's meeting. I leave the office at 5:00. But it's not the last I see of my work mates. As it's Monday night, it's Binnie Black & Veatch football night!"

Helen Keeble - South West Water Microbiology Department

"I joined South West Water in the summer break of 1993 to gain work experience between the second and final years of my degree. I returned after graduation (in September 1994) as a Laboratory Assistant and was quickly trained in all microbiological techniques for water, food and parasite analyses. I was promoted to Technician in 1995 and was given responsibility for the validation of a new Cryptosporidium membrane filtration technique. I took a career break at the end of 1997 to travel, spending 3 months working in microbiology for AWT Ensight (New South Wales Water Company) in Sydney.

I returned to South West Water in January 1999 and was trained in Flow Cytometry and microscopy for Cryptosporidium and Giardia detection. This allowed others to concentrate on validation of the new DWI Cryptosporidium method which went live

The Casella Group is a rapidly expanding group of companies providing high quality environmental technologies and services across the built and natural environments.

Employing over 850 specialists in the UK and with a presence in over 60 countries world-wide The Casella Group is a market leader.

To find out more about our comprehensive range of services and products and to see our current recruitment opportunities visit us at www.casellagroup.com

CASELLA≡

These services are part of a wider range of environmental services and instrumentation available from the Casella Group.

Offices throughout the UK

Gemma Woplin, Regent House, Wolseley Road, Kempston, Bedford, MK42 7JY.
Telephone: 01234 844100 Facsimile: 01234 841490 Email: info@casellagroup.com

www.casellagroup.com   **Think environment   Think Casella** in April 2000. On introduction of the new method, I was made a Senior Assistant Scientist in the Cryptosporidium section and was promoted again to Scientist in September 2000. Since then I have been in charge of the Cryptosporidium section, ensuring compliance to a forensic standard of analysis, in line with the regulatory demands. I represent South West Water on a national Cryptosporidium Regulatory Analytical Group (CRAG) and I am significantly involved in the preparation and liaison with the Drinking Water Inspectorate (DWI) during audits.

After an eight-year laboratory based career, I have successfully gained a transfer to the Potable Science Quality Department. My responsibilities in the new post will include providing scientific and process advice to water treatment and water distribution departments and carrying out investigation work within the potable water function."

Contacts

Association of Consulting Engineers
12 Caxton Street, London SW1HOQL
Tel: 020 7222 6557
www.acenet.co.uk

Binnie Black & Veatch Ltd
Grosvenor House, 69 London Road, Redhill, Surrey, RH1 1LQ
Tel: 01737 774155
www.bbv-ltd.com

Cleverly Consulting
E-mail: graham@cleverly.co.uk
www.cleverly.co.uk

Drinking Water Inspectorate
Floor 2/A1, Ashdown House, 123 Victoria Street, London, SW1E 6DE
Tel: 020 7944 5956
www.dwi.gov.uk

Department for Environment, Food and Rural Affairs (DEFRA)
Eland House, Bressenden Place, London SWIE 5DU
Tel: 020 8903000
www.defra.gov.uk

Department for International Development
1 Palace Street, London, SW1E 5HE
Tel: 020 7023 0000
www.dfid.gov.uk

Environment Agency
Rio House, Waterside Drive, Aztec West, Almondsbury, Bristol BS32 4UD
Tel: 01454 624 400
www.environment-agency.gov.uk

European Environment Agency
Kongens Nytorv 6, 1050 Copenhagen K, Denmark
Tel: +45 33367100,
www.eea.eu.int

The European Union On-line
www.europa.eu.int

OFWAT
Centre City Tower, 7 Hill Street, Birmingham B5 4UA
Tel: 0121 625 1300
www.ofwat.gov.uk (This website includes a list of water companies and addresses)

Scottish Water
PO Box 8855, Edinburgh, EH10 6YQ
Tel: 0845 6018855
www.scottishwater.co.uk

Voluntary Service Overseas
317 Putney Bridge Road, London, SW15 2PN
Tel: 020 8780 7200
www.vso.org.uk

WaterAid
Prince Consort House, 27-29 Albert Embankment, London SE1 7UB
Tel: 020 7793 4500
www.wateraid.org.uk

Water UK
1 Queen Annes Gate, London SW1H 9BT
Tel: 020 7344 1827/1811
www.water.org.uk

Water Research Centre (WRc)
Franklands Road, Blagrove, Swindon, Wiltshire, SN5 8YF
Tel: 01793 865000.
www.wrcplc.co.uk

References

Drinking Water Inspectorate (2002) Drinking Water 2001: *A report by the Chief Inspector Drinking Water Inspectorate. London: HMSO.*

Tearfund and WaterAid (2002) The Human Waste: *A call for urgent action to combat the millions of deaths caused by poor sanitation.*

Innovation, value and out-turn certainty. Looking to the future

Programme management solutions
Environmental engineering services
Drainage modelling and flow surveying
Fine bubble and mechanical aeration
Leakage management
Membrane biological reactors
OTT high efficiency diffused aeration

Biwater

telephone +44 (0)1706 367555   www.biwater.co.uk

16. Pipeline Networks

David Bowen, Biwater

The Sector

Pipeline networks are the underground conduits for clean water and wastewater. At around 350,000km of water pipes and a similar length of sewer pipes in the UK, they represent more than 50% of the asset value of the water companies today. As water pipes have an asset life of 100 years, 1% should be replaced each year at a cost of £400m, plus a similar figure for maintenance, and the same again for sewers - a huge undertaking.

Water pipeline networks distribute the water from the water treatment works to the taps of the domestic and commercial water users, through metallic and non-metallic pipes. Typical pipe diameters range from 1000mm to 25mm at the customers tap end. Pipe networks also bring the water to the treatment works from various sources - river intakes, impounding reservoirs collecting upland stream water, and boreholes where the water is pumped from underground aquifers. These water channels tend to be in larger diameter pipes, aqueducts or tunnels, where the water usually travels under gravity, unlike the distribution pipes, which are predominantly pressurised.

Wastewater pipes take sewage away from properties to the sewage treatment works, from which large pipes or culverts discharge the cleaned water to streams or rivers, or into the sea. Sewerage pipe dimensions tend to be larger - from 100mm to 2 metres and usually non-metallic, unless pumped.

Managing pipe networks requires design knowledge for new pipelines, refurbishment of existing pipelines and analysis of the network to determine the effect of age and demand - which could lead to bursts, poor water quality or inadequate pressure. The pipeline engineer needs to specify the appropriate materials for the operating conditions and the ground conditions to ensure the pipe meets its design life requirements and ensure it is correctly laid and commissioned, maintained, inspected and repaired, to satisfy the Office of Water Services (OFWAT) standards.

Sector Profile

It is difficult to estimate how many people are employed on pipelines as many have additional responsibilities, but the figure is probably around 20,000. These will range from experienced but non-technical operatives to administrators and designers to senior engineers or managers. As efficiencies and technologies improve, the number of pipe operatives will reduce as will the number of senior and design engineers, but opportunities for qualified engineers, able to use the computer software analysis packages, are likely to increase in number.

Typical Post Names

Pipeline Design Engineer, Rehabilitation Engineer, Operations Engineer, Contracts Engineer, Network Analysis Engineer, Drawing Office Manager, Pipelines Engineer, Road Opening Notice Technician, Draughtsman, Technical Assistant.

Main Employers

Water Companies, Water Industry Consultants, Pipeline Contractors, Pipe Manufacturers, Specialist Research organisations, also comparable Gas and Petrochemical organisations.

Career Opportunities

Pipeline Network careers can start at any level. At the practical level, this can involve laying pipes to managing major pipe laying contracts. At the technical level, work assisting the design of major pipelines will require ONC or HNC level qualifications, and supervising or managing the project will require a Civil Engineering degree or similar and probably Chartered status for the more technically demanding projects. For Network Analysis, an HNC or degree in Engineering or Computing would be appropriate.

Issues and Trends

Water companies have a significant number of pipeline engineering staff who tend to carry out the strategic infrastructure assessment of pipeline performance and standards internally. However, the installation work has been increasingly issued to contractors through competitive tender since privatisation in 1990, due to cost cutting and implementation of new technologies and methodologies which is best achieved in the outside market place.

This work initially involved major pipeline work, but water companies have now increased the scale of contracting to include annual main-laying and maintenance contracts. On the design side, similarly, initially only major pipe-laying projects were designed and managed by consulting engineers, but more recently design, supervision and management of the smaller projects, plus network analysis and leak detection, are now carried out by consultants.

Personal Profiles

John Westerman - Principal Operations Engineer - Age 50, Chartered Engineer with Technology Degree and HND/C in Civil Engineering, Member of the Chartered Institution of Water and Environmental Management (CIWEM), the Institution of Civil Engineers (ICE) and the Institution of Water Officers (IWO). 30 years experience with 3 water companies and a Consulting/Contractor organisation. Duties involve Client/Project management of Scottish INMS Operations, English and Irish leak detection and DMA projects, overseas consultancy for rehabilitation and due diligence and business development to meet clients consultancy demands.

Mike Southern - Operations Engineer - Age 29, Civil and Structural Engineering graduate, nearing chartered status. Project engineer with a Consulting /Contracting organisation, 6 years experience in Network Analysis (Infoworks/WESNET/Stoner), Data management including GIS applications and Fieldwork for logging, Network Pressure Reduction projects and Leak Detection for English, Scottish and Overseas clients. Training new graduates for modelling and team building.

Peter Northall - Senior Leakage Technician - Age 28, BTEC Diploma in Business/Finance, City & Guilds in Water Distribution, including Leakage monitoring/tracing/correlation and acoustic detection, plus signing lighting & guarding. Team

Leader with a Consulting/Contracting organisation, 8 years experience in Leak Detection, step testing, DMA fieldwork audit, meter verification, customer liaison and reporting for many English/Scottish and overseas clients - working closely with other consultants in a specialist capacity.

Contacts

All UK Water Companies have personnel departments with information on career opportunities for pipeline networks engineers. Access to the water companies can be achieved via the water company web sites and the website of Water UK, which is the organisation which represents the water companies (www.water.org.uk).

Association of Consulting Engineers
www.acenet.co.uk

The Chartered Institution of Water and Environmental Management (CIWEM)
www.ciwem.com

Biwater
www.biwater.co.uk

British Water
www.britishwater.co.uk

Drinking Water Inspectorate (DWI)
www.dwi.gov.uk

Environment Agency
www.environment-agency.gov.uk

Institution of Water Officers (IWO)
www.iwo.org.uk

Office of Water Services (OFWAT)
www.ofwat.gov.uk

Pipeline Industries Guild (PIG)
www.pipeguild.co.uk

Society of British Water and Wastewater Industries (SBWWI)
www.sbwi.co.uk

Magazines with interest in the water industry include the institution periodicals - CIWEM journal, IWO journal, NCE magazine, PIG Pipeline World, Water Bulletin, Water and Wastewater, WET News, World Water and many others.

17. Water Quality & Pollution Control

Graham Cleverly, Independent Water & Environmental Consultant

The Sector

The occurrence and control of water pollution is a vital issue in almost all parts of the world, even in the remote Arctic and Antarctic regions. This is largely a result of human activities and sometimes made worse by extreme weather events. Water pollution can occur in all water bodies i.e. groundwater, inland surface water, coastal and territorial waters.

We all depend on the quality of our fresh water for life as well as for important activities such as irrigation, industrial use, energy generation, washing, cleaning and recreation. Water also provides a vital habitat for freshwater and marine plants and animals.

The key issue is how well we can manage the whole water and land environment in an integrated and sustainable manner to avoid or minimise pollution. Addressing this issue properly will ensure that our precious water resources are available in sufficient quality (and quantity) throughout the world to meet our needs and the needs of future generations.

In the UK, we have established environmental water quality objectives and a comprehensive legislative framework over many years for monitoring and controlling water resources and minimising pollution impacts. About a third of the water used for drinking purposes in the UK comes from our underground water resources and special measures have recently been put in place to protect this vulnerable resource from pollution.

Pollution originates from two main sources: point sources and diffuse sources. *Point* pollution (e.g. polluted untreated process water from a factory discharging into a river) is much easier to identify and address than *diffuse* pollution (e.g. pollution to an underground aquifer from applications of excess pesticides or fertilizer by a farmer to his land).

As point sources of pollution are increasingly controlled, mainly through huge investment in treatment by the water industry since privatisation in 1989 and similar investment by industry through Integrated Pollution Control and Integrated Pollution Prevention and Control, the focus is shifting to addressing the more intractable diffuse pollution issues.

Some *key issues* in monitoring and controlling water pollution include:
- Understanding the main causes of water pollution from a variety of both point and diffuse sources and their impacts on water bodies;
- Having a comprehensive set of environmental water quality standards and discharge consents in place;
- Ensuring that the discharges of the most dangerous chemicals are rigorously controlled, to avoid groundwater pollution;
- Having a robust and transparent system to monitor and report publicly on the quality (and quantity) of all water bodies;
- Having a comprehensive set of laws, regulations, planning procedures and codes of practice. These measures ensure that there is a clear and

consistent framework for controlling pollution through the provision of advice and guidance and ultimately prosecution of individuals and organisations who knowingly pollute or cause pollution to occur to our water bodies;
- Educating industry, agriculture, local authorities and the public on pollution prevention.

Sector Profile

It is difficult to estimate the total number of people engaged in water pollution control activities in the UK. Many people have duties which include the prevention and control of pollution as part of a wider role. Examples include farmers (who maintain their silage stores to ensure than no overflows escape into rivers), factory site managers (who ensure that polluted process water is not flushed down the wrong drain and into rivers) and waste disposal contractors (who ensure that leachate from landfill sites is controlled and does not escape into groundwater or surface waters).

Those working more directly in the monitoring and control of water pollution include:
- The environmental regulators (e.g. Environment Agency) who are responsible for monitoring possible pollution events and following up and warning or prosecuting serious pollution offenders;
- Laboratory/field technicians responsible for sampling and analysing water samples;
- Researchers, business environment advisors, Non Governmental Organisations (NGOs) and pressure groups, local authorities, government/ Department for the Environment, Food and Rural Affairs (DEFRA).

In addition there are special co-ordinated Local Authority and emergency services teams responsible for public safety and emergency pollution control measures arising from major incidents (e.g. road accidents involving tankers carrying dangerous chemicals).

Typical Post Names

- Environment Protection Officer (environmental regulators) *
- Environment Protection Assistants (environmental regulators)
- Laboratory staff (environmental regulators and private laboratories)
- Wastewater Treatment Plant Manager (water and wastewater utilities)
- Site Environmental Manager - often covering Health and Safety and environment (industry/ waste management)
- Environmental Health Officer (Local Authority)
- Environment Business Advisor (Non Governmental Organisations e.g. Groundwork)

Main Employers

The main employers for pollution control activities in the UK are the *environmental regulators* who undertake the role of 'guardians' of the environment. They carry out a wide range of tasks associated with pollution control through powers given to them by various Parliamentary Acts and Regulations. They regulate all industrial pollution emissions, including water pollution as well as pollution to air and land, by some 7000 major industrial installations (e.g. chemical plants) and have special powers to control and minimise pollution of our groundwater resources.

In England and Wales, the *Environment Agency* has a statutory responsibility to, amongst other things, maintain or improve the quality of fresh, marine, surface and underground water. This responsibility includes monitoring and controlling the pollution of all waters and ensuring that our water resources are managed in a sustainable manner. Out of a total Environment Agency staff of 10,000, there are:

- 1000 Environment Protection Officers* plus around 400 staff engaged on water pollution monitoring;
- Several hundred lab staff;
- Over a thousand ancillary staff - managers, technical support, policy development, Research and Development (R & D), Marine and Special Projects, groundwater modelling, contaminated land, education, campaigns, planning.

* At the time of writing, reorganisation of the Environment Agency was underway to develop multi-functional field delivery teams including Environment Officers (formerly Environment Protection Officers) and staff from fisheries, water resources and other fields.

Following the devolution of some Government responsibilities including environmental protection, the *Scottish Environment Protection Agency (SEPA)* in Scotland and the *Department of the Environment* in Northern Ireland have similar responsibilities to the Environment Agency for controlling and preventing pollution and offer similar employment opportunities.

Other employers where pollution control is part of wider environmental activities include:

- Water Utilities
- Consultancies
- Local Authorities
- Waste Disposal Contractors
- Industry
- Farming and Wildlife Advisory Group (FWAG)
- Pressure Groups/Non Governmental Organisations (NGOs) e.g. Greenpeace
- Universities/commercial research bodies e.g. Water Research Centre (WRc)

Career Opportunities

The environmental regulators take on a wide range of graduates and school leavers with an interest in the environment. For example, Environment Protection Assistants (EPAs) employed by the Environment Agency need a broad educational background with either a Degree or 'A' levels as well as relevant experience. They need excellent inter-personal, diplomatic and communications skills, and the ability to influence and negotiate with a wide range of people and promote the Agency's vision. They must also be capable of working efficiently when unsupervised and able to manage their own time effectively. See the Personal Profiles section for more information about working in Environment Protection for the Environment Agency.

Environment Protection Assistant (EPA) starting salaries range from £12,000 to £13,500 and Environment Protection Officer (EPO) starting salaries are in the range £15,000 to £20,500. New graduates receive structured competency based training and staff development. Other benefits include flexi-working, generous holiday entitlement and pensions. See the Environment Agency website (details in the Contacts section) for job opportunities.

Consultant opportunities are more fully described in Chapter 15 on Drinking Water Quality & Wastewater Management.

Issues and Trends

The UK has a long history of industrial activity and associated pollution but its rainy climate, fast flowing rivers and long and turbulent tidal coastline have often mitigated the worst effects of water pollution. Environmental legislation in the UK has traditionally been characterised by considerable flexibility with a preference for locally set, variable water quality standards to suit the capacity of the receiving water and take some account of the effects of diffuse pollution. Elsewhere in Europe centrally set emission standards have been the norm.

However, European Directives which embrace sustainability and the 'polluter pays' principle have driven much of the recent UK environmental legislation including water pollution control. The next few years will see the setting of statutory water quality objectives for all inland surface waters together with a more holistic and integrated approach to managing our water resources, arising from the implementation of the *Water Framework Directive*. This important Directive covers all water bodies and promotes water resource management on a river catchment basis with the long-term aim of achieving 'good water quality status' in all waters by 2015. The UK environmental regulators played a key part in developing this Directive, sometimes known in Brussels as 'the British Directive', and it has adopted many principles pioneered in the UK including river basin management and a combination of emission standards and water quality objectives.

Future challenges
Alongside routine monitoring and control of pollution, future challenges to water pollution control in the UK include:
- Setting and meeting statutory water quality objectives
- Meeting the requirements of the Integrated Pollution Prevention and Control (IPPC) Directive, the Water Framework Directive and other important Directives affecting water quality
- Reducing diffuse pollution from agriculture by implementing more integrated pollution control measures
- Greater coordination of pollution prevention measures at Government level and thorough cost-benefit analysis
- Wider application of economic instruments to reduce water pollution e.g. subsidies to prevent farmers applying excess nitrates to soils and maybe a pesticides tax.
- Educating industry (particularly small and medium size enterprises)
- Increasing the application of Sustainable Urban Drainage Systems (SUDS)
- Coping with impacts of new emergencies (e.g. Foot and Mouth Disease) on water pollution

Overseas opportunities
Overseas, the huge challenge of delivering clean drinking water and sanitation to the world's expanding urban and rural populations is increasingly focussing on protecting their scarce water resources from pollution. Opportunities to work overseas with voluntary organisations (such as Voluntary Service Overseas) as well as commercial consultancies and aid organisations will continue to grow for practitioners with some experience.

Posts similar to Environment Protection Officer exist in developed countries including Australia, New Zealand and the USA. Enlargement of the European Union is also providing limited opportunities for experienced water pollution control staff to assist transition countries in Central and Eastern Europe in implementing and applying European Environmental Directives including key water Directives.

Personal Profiles

Nick Hepworth - Hydrogeologist, Environment Agency

"I gained an Upper Second Class BSc (Hons) degree in Environmental Sciences from the University of East Anglia in 1993, and joined the National Rivers Authority (now the Environment Agency) in 1995 as a Hydrology Officer after voluntary work overseas and a spell as a voluntary teacher at a Field Studies Centre.

After a year working in Water Resources I transferred to the Environmental Protection function, serving initially as an Assistant Pollution Control Officer and later as Environment Protection Officer on the Ribble catchment in Lancashire until 1999. Together with proactive pollution prevention work, my responsibilities there included the investigation and remediation of pollution incidents, taking prosecutions in line with the Agency's enforcement policy, and carrying out compliance inspections and monitoring at water treatment works, waste management installations, industrial sites and on farms.

I then worked as Project Manager of the Agency's Millennium Festival Project which involved working with local communities to deliver participatory environmental improvements. This included the Padiham Weir Project, involving the creation of a fish pass and canoe run to rehabilitate the River Calder catchment and so make best use of improved water quality. From 2000 to 2002 I was Groundwater Protection Officer in the same region where I was responsible for the roll out of the Groundwater Regulations and carrying out regulatory inspections and pollution prevention campaigns.

I am currently working as a Hydrogeologist in the Agency's Thames Region, where I am responsible for hydrological investigations and assessments to ensure sustainable groundwater resource management across a complex hydrogeological area. I am also engaged in research and development work within the Agency looking at how environmental protection messages can be marketed more effectively.

I will shortly complete my Masters Degree in Water and Environmental Resource Management for which I have studied part time at Liverpool John Moores University. In 1999, I gained the CIWEM accredited Postgraduate Diploma in Water and Environmental Management also at Liverpool John Moores University, where I am now the course leader for the Water Pollution Control module.

I have also worked in a voluntary capacity as a consultant to WaterAid in Tanzania where I provided advice on the protection of groundwater resources serving the city of Dar es Salaam."

Tracey Smith - Monitoring Officer (Environment Protection), Environment Agency

"I joined the National Rivers Authority (now the Environment Agency) in 1992, initially as a Technical Assistant (Water Quality) following 6 years working with industrial chemical companies in the north west as an Analytical Chemist/Research Technician after leaving school.

My next post with the Environment Agency was Scientific Support Officer (Environment Planning), where I worked with the landfill engineering team and gained experience in modern landfill design and operational issues.

In my current role as Monitoring Officer (Environment Protection) at the Agency's Sale office in Cheshire, I have been instrumental in developing the water quality capabilities of Environment Protection staff and providing training in support of the recent launch of the Agency's updated National Sampling Procedures Manual.

After leaving school with 9 GCSEs, I gained an ONC (Science) qualification followed by an HNC (Chemistry) on day release at Blackburn Technical College and the Managing the Environment Open University qualification. I subsequently studied part time at Bolton Institute where I gained qualifications in Contaminated Land Reclamation and Geotechnical Engineering. I also gained a Diploma in Pollution Control through the Open University.

As part of my continued professional development I gained the top UK mark in the CIWEM Certificate at Liverpool John Moores University in 2001/2002 and I am now studying for the CIWEM Diploma."

Steven Smith - Environment Protection Officer, Environment Agency

"My current role is to provide an integrated service in the delivery of pollution prevention and control in the Upper Mersey area by the control and regulation of polluting activities including: waste management, consenting discharges, agricultural, commercial and industrial facilities. I am also involved in incident response activities on waste and water pollution events including investigations, collection of evidence and any subsequent monitoring.

I was previously employed as a Quality Control Technician with William Blythe Ltd for 5 years where I was responsible for all environmental testing at their Hapton site, then with the National Rivers Authority as an Environmental Monitoring Officer.

After leaving school in 1985 with 6 'O' Level and 2 GCSE certificates, I attended Blackburn College where I gained BTEC National and Higher Certificates in Science. I then went on to study with the Open University, gaining qualifications in Environmental Control, Environmental Modelling and a Diploma in Pollution Control. I completed a BSc at the Open University in 2001.

As part of my continued professional development I gained the third highest UK mark in the CIWEM Certificate at Liverpool John Moores University in 2001/2002. I am currently studying for the CIWEM Diploma and for an MSc in Water, Energy and the Environment."

Joanne Startin - Process Compliance Manager, United Utilities

"I joined United Utilities (then North West Water) in 1989 after completing my full time academic studies at Lancaster Polytechnic where I gained an HND in Chemistry. I worked in laboratory services until 1995, analysing water and wastewater operational and regulatory samples from over 600 wastewater treatment works and over 200 water treatment works.

In 1995 I moved to operations, as Water Quality Scientist, where I was responsible for analysing drinking water results from the laboratory and interpreting them for our customers and regulators. In 1997 I moved to asset management as a Wastewater Analytical Planner, where I was wholelife project manager for capital schemes for wastewater treatment works and the sewerage network in the West Lancashire area. In 1999 I then moved back into operations as Senior Process Controller for Central Lancashire Wastewater. There I undertook a team leader role, responsible for the compliance of wastewater treatment works in the central Lancashire area.

In 2001 I was promoted to Process Compliance Manager for North Lancashire Wastewater, now United Utilities. I am now responsible for a large area with some 46 wastewater treatment works and 15 wastewater pumping stations. I am responsible for ensuring these assets meet all regulatory outputs, including consent to discharge, the Urban Wastewater Treatment Directive and the Bathing Water Directive.

I have also completed the CIWEM Certificate and Diploma and followed this up with an MSc in Water, Energy and the Environment from Liverpool John Moores University in 2001."

A day in the life of an Environment Protection Officer with the Environment Agency
Jane - Environment Protection Officer, Midlands Region

"One of the best things about my job is the variety. In the morning I could be meeting a Managing Director to discuss the redevelopment of a contaminated land site and in the afternoon I might be investigating fly tipping or water pollution. Dealing with a wide range of people you need to have a flexible approach.

In a nutshell, my job is a balance between enforcing environmental laws and promoting environmental pollution prevention.

Once every 2 or 3 months I take part in the emergency out-of-hours rota. This can be quite challenging and exciting as we deal with pollution incidents. As you are potentially the only person on site representing the Agency, so you need to use your own initiative and problem-solving skills. You have to organise resources, do a bit of 'detective' work to track down the source of the problem and deal with the emergency services.

I have a lot of freedom to organise my own workload whilst still enjoying the support of my colleagues in the team. The people I work with are the best in their field and when I meet people socially they're usually really interested in what I do and what the Agency is about. Our team is multi-skilled but people also have their own specialisms, which usually tie in with their personal interests, such as contaminated land or agriculture.

Environment Agency staff have a personal development plan to assist them to reach their potential in the organisation. I was given the opportunity to step into my Team Leader's role, which was a good way of getting some management experience.

There's lots of training and support provided for new Environment Protection Officers. The Agency has a structured competency-training programme with modules that are designed to support individual and team development needs tailored to suit you. You also learn a lot by 'doing it' on the job. During the first six months you work towards getting your warrant and gaining an overview of the job. After that it's all about building on your knowledge and skills."

Contacts

Cleverly Consulting
E-mail: graham@cleverly.co.uk
www.cleverly.co.uk

Environment Agency (EA)
HQ: Rio House, Waterside Drive, Aztec, West, Almondsbury, Bristol, BS32 4UD
Tel: 01454 624 400.
www.environment-agency.gov.uk/jobs

Groundwork
Groundwork UK, 85-87 Cornwall Street, Birmingham, B3 3BY
Tel: 0121 236 8565
www.groundwork.org.uk

Institute of Ecology and Environmental Management
45 Southgate Street, Winchester, Hants SO23 9EH
Tel: 01962 868626
www.ieem.co.uk

Institute of Wastes Management
9 Saxon Court, St Peter's Gardens, Northampton, NN1 1SX
Tel: 01604 620426
www.iwm.co.uk

Scottish Environment Protection Agency (SEPA)
Corporate Office, Erskine Court, Castle Business Park, Stirling, FK9 4TR
Tel: 01786 457700.
www.sepa.org.uk

Water Research Centre (WRc)
Franklands Road, Blagrove, Swindon, Wiltshire, SN5 8YF
Tel: 01793 865000.
www.wrplc.co.uk

Water UK
1 Queen Anne's Gate, London, SW1H 9BT
Tel: 020 7344 1827/1811
www.water.org.uk

Voluntary Service Overseas (VSO)
317 Putney Bridge Road, London, SW15 2PN
Tel: 020 8780 7200
E-mail: enquiry@vso.org.uk
www.vso.org.uk

18.   The Sub-Surface Environment: Groundwater & Contaminated Land

Bob Harris, Environment Agency

The Sector

The sub-surface is a discrete area of the environment that calls for sound scientific understanding to underpin the UK's approach to risk-based decision-making. Groundwater and soils are both environmental resources that require protection and remediation when polluted. Wrong decisions based on poor knowledge can be highly costly to both the regulated community and UK industry as a whole. The decision-making must therefore be knowledge-based.

Groundwater provides approximately one third of the nation's drinking water supply. However, this proportion is highly variable throughout the country and increases greatly towards the south-east corner of the country where the regional reliance increases to nearly 80%. Most people receive a supply from their Water Company, which often blends the water from various sources or boreholes. However, there are also many towns and villages that are completely dependent on a single groundwater source. There are also an estimated 100,000 households in England and Wales who have their own discrete private supply.

Groundwater is vulnerable to pollution from surface activities because it is out of sight and therefore often out of mind. It occurs in all rocks and therefore the threats to groundwater quality, and, in the case of its use in water supply, to people's health, can come from *any* activity on the land surface. The biggest acute threats are presented by the infiltration of pathogens and chemical point source releases (such as chemical spills, accidents, uncontained waste storage etc) while chronic effects accumulate through diffuse pollution (nitrate, pesticides etc). The quantities of chemicals involved can be very small, since we use precautionary health-based standards for drinking water. So, for example, it only takes 1 litre of a common industrial solvent such as trichloroethylene to contaminate a quantity of water equivalent to 80 Olympic-sized swimming pools such that the safe drinking water level is exceeded.

For groundwater the sector can neatly be divided into 3 in terms of environmental interests. The skills required for these are very similar since a strong basis in hydrogeology is required for each:
· The abstraction of groundwater and the impact of this on aquatic and terrestrial ecosystems (many geoscientists are also employed by the mineral extraction and mining industries);
· The prevention of pollution of groundwater from diffuse (e.g. agricultural land use) and point sources (e.g. chemical and fuel manufacturing/storage);
· The remediation of historically polluted groundwater.

Soil is a precious resource that plays many roles. It is vital for food production. All the earth's vegetation is dependent on soil for the supply of nutrients and water and for root fixation. Soil is a storehouse of minerals, organic matter, water and energy, and also a potential sink for pollutants. It is a water filter, a transformer of gases and a gene pool for a huge variety of organisms. For all these reasons, soil needs to be protected on an equal footing with water and air. At present activity on the environmental protection of soil, as opposed to its agricultural use, is limited. New legislation is developing within Europe, but most activity currently relates to the remediation of polluted soils. For many circumstances understanding about soil and groundwater remediation has to be closely related and many of the skills required will be common.

The sub-surface is highly complex in terms of our scientific and technical understanding. Regardless of the origin of the infiltrating recharge water (rainfall or an anthropogenically-induced discharge) or the chemical fluxes within the soil, aquifer or landfill, an understanding of the processes requires the ability to conceptualise events and make decisions based on minimal data. It is always expensive to gather data about the subsurface and invariably the amount one has is insufficient to give certainty. For pollution control purposes a consideration and understanding about the movement of a pollutant species dissolved within a liquid media, water or another solvent, is required. The pollutant is also travelling within a solid medium (the soil or aquifer) and it is all out of sight perhaps several tens or hundreds of metres below the ground surface. Brain surgeons might sometimes have more information!

Sector Profile

The legislation that affects the sub-surface and therefore to a large extent drives interest in it has mushroomed over the past 5 years. This has resulted in, and will continue to fuel, a large growth in the market for sub-surface environmental specialists. Decision-making in this sector in the UK has moved from a pseudo-voluntary to a regulatory risk-based approach, that requires a much more sure-footed and scientifically based approach. The following relevant legislation has been introduced or is forthcoming:
- Groundwater Regulations 1998
- Section 161A of the Water Resources Act 1991, Works Notices
- Part IIA of the Environmental Protection Act 1990 (Contaminated Land Regulations)
- Integrated Pollution Prevention and Control (IPPC) Directive and associated regulations
- Landfill Directive and associated regulations
- Water Framework Directive (to be implemented in 2002 and phased in over a period)
- Environmental Liability Directive (still being negotiated in 2002)
- Soil Protection Communication (likely to lead to new legislation on soil protection)

A significant proportion of the revenue of consultancies now comes from contaminated land projects and those concerning the below-ground environment e.g. water pollution, and this pattern is reflected in the expertise of employees.

In 2002 therefore the market for this sector is very buoyant. Those with appropriate postgraduate degrees will find it very easy to obtain jobs since demand has outstripped supply. The increasing trend is expected to continue for the foreseeable future with the introduction of new European legislation, the increasing focus on diffuse pollution and the application and take-up of recent UK regulations, which have yet to bite in full. The sub-surface environment has suffered from significant under-investment and lack of attention in the UK until recently and the current interest is a reflection of the change that is taking place.

Typical Post Names

Hydrogeologist, Hydrogeochemist, Contaminated Land Officer, Geotechical Officer, Soil Scientist, Scientific Support Officer (Hydrogeology), Groundwater Quality Officer, Groundwater Protection Officer.

Main Employers

There are 1000 or more professionally qualified geoscientists working in this sector within the UK. The majority will be hydrogeologists but many will have qualifications in geochemistry, soil science, geotechnical engineering, mining geology etc and will have acquired practical experience of applying their knowledge in real situations. Within the regulatory sector there are around 300 to 400, with a similar (or greater) number found in consultancies. A few will be employed by industry (particularly the Water Industry and those large blue-chip companies who have a legacy of contaminated land) but, by and large, industry seeks these specialist skills from consultants rather than employing them in-house.

Regulators: Environment Agency, Scottish Environment Protection Agency, Local Authorities. Around 300-400 employed.

Consultancies: Most of the main environmental consultancies will employ hydrogeologists and contaminated land remediation specialists. The large engineering based consultancies will also employ them, although some will subcontract specialist skills (for example in bioremediation of groundwater). Most will also employ other geoscientists, particularly in the fields of geotechnical engineering and site investigation. Around 300-500 employed.

Industry: The Water Industry employs hydrogeologists to advise on the abstraction of groundwater and its protection from pollution. Heavy manufacturing industry also employs contaminated land specialists where there is significant interest in dealing with a contaminated land legacy. Such companies tend to have larger land-holdings (e.g. Lattice Properties) or have world-wide interests (e.g. BP, Shell). Around 20-50 employed.

Others: Few sub-surface specialists will be found outside of the three main employing sectors above, except for within Research Institutes, such as the British Geological Survey, and specialist academic departments in universities such as Sheffield, Queens University, Belfast, Newcastle, Birmingham, and Reading. These groups increasingly undertake consultancy work in association with their research as they begin to deal more with "real world" issues as opposed to pure research. Around 100 employed.

Career Opportunities

The sub-surface environment calls for discrete skills of the technical specialists who work in it. The professional background required is often similar with most people having a first, and most often a postgraduate, degree in some form of earth sciences (geology, geotechnology, engineering geology, geophysics, geochemistry, hydrogeology, soil science etc).

To progress in a career in this sector you would therefore be advised to graduate in one of the earth sciences, although to progress onto a Masters course or to undertake a PhD this is not essential. A science based degree such as chemistry, microbiology or mathematics would provide a solid basis from which to specialise. However, a postgraduate degree is strongly advised and there is plenty of choice depending on the chosen career path. For the water and environment industries the most popular course is to take a Masters degree in hydrogeology, although it should be noted that the number of courses (and therefore places) has been reduced of late and competition is intense. Good first degree students who apply to potential employers beforehand may be lucky in attracting sponsorship, but if successful this will tie you to the employer for an initial period.

Within the regulatory community the technical experts at local and national level provide their technical expertise to the staff who actually negotiate and process the application or consultation by which the regulator or Local Authority is communicating its views or decisions. Their skills essentially apply to technical, scientific or engineering knowledge whilst the other necessary skills in decision-making are regulatory process or procedurally based. These roles are discrete but often the technical advice is so fundamental that the whole decision-making relies on it. At other times procedural issues dominate. Opportunities exist, within the Environment Agencies particularly, to move between the purely technical and the decision-making areas and progress into a wider management role.

For entry-level geologists, hydrogeologists, or geotechnical jobs, which usually require postgraduate degrees, the starting salaries are around £15,000 to £18,000. This rises to an average of £20,000 to £22,000 with 2 years experience and £27,000 to £30,000 with 5 years of experience.

The private and public sectors have very different profiles at present since the public sector has not caught up with the market and pays substantially lower salaries than the private sector. There is some movement between the public and private sectors in both directions. With 10 years of experience, salaries offered are in the £30,000 to £40,000 and above range. For very experienced and able people the rewards can be considerable. For good technical staff their specialist skills and knowledge will be marketable with most employers.

A large number of hydrogeological and other earth sciences orientated staff will be members of the Geological Society and can become Chartered Geologists. European Geologist status is also available. CIWEM offers an additional or separate professional body whilst other people are members of the Institution of Civil Engineers or associated professional bodies, specific to their original discipline. The requirement to become a corporate or Chartered member of an appropriate professional body to ensure career progression is variable throughout the sector.

One new qualification has been introduced recently, Specialist in Land Contamination (SiLC), which is for experienced individuals who by qualifying and registering as a SiLC will be able to complete Land Condition Records (LCRs). The use of a registered SiLC will give the highest level of credibility to the information contained in a LCR. This is possibly a foretaste of a time when specialist professional qualifications may be required for people to perform at the highest levels of their profession.

Issues and Trends

Groundwater: Groundwater is likely to take more of a front seat in environmental issues in the future. The introduction of the European Water Framework Directive will emphasise the need to ensure that we are more integrated in our approach to water management in future. Thus quantity and quality, and groundwater and surface water issues will need to be considered in concert. Many of our lowland river systems are driven by groundwater baseflows. For example 60% of the dry-weather freshwater flow of the River Thames in its downstream reaches has passed through the groundwater system. This has major implications for how we manage the associated catchments, particularly for diffuse pollution.

Contaminated Land: The contaminated land legislation in the UK is very new and the UK through its Local Authorities and regulators is still trying to understand the extent of the problem and the scale of intervention needed. Private industry continues to take the liability issues very seriously and this and other non-regulatory drivers, such as the government's commitment to have 60% of new housing built on brownfield land, will be as, if not more, significant as the legislation in promoting the issues. Contaminated land is set to continue at a high profile and we have as much of a legacy as most developed countries to address. The investigation of sites, whether contaminated or not, will a remain variable market which is very dependent on the economy and the need for redevelopment on brownfield or greenfield sites.

Soil Protection: Newly awakened interest in soil protection will demand a focus on soil that has so far been lacking in the UK. Although legislation in the shape of the contaminated land regime, the Integrated Pollution Prevention and Control Directive and the new Environmental Liability Directive already addresses soil protection and clean-up in a small way, it will be interesting to watch how new European initiatives promote the need for increased work in this area.

Overseas Opportunities: Internationally the UK has a high profile in this sector. We spend more on research than most European countries, have a respected risk-based regulatory regime, were the first to adopt catchment management in a significant way and have a buoyant consultancy sector working throughout the world. There are consequently many opportunities to market and exploit UK expertise and working abroad is a possibility for those who wish it.

Personal Profiles

Gordon Lethbridge - Principal Consultant, Environment Section, HSE Consultancy Group, Shell Global Solutions

"I have more than 25 years experience in the behaviour, fate and effects of chemicals in soils and groundwaters and their natural and engineered removal from these environments. After graduating from the University of Kent at Canterbury in 1974 with a First Class Honours Degree in Microbiology, I stayed on to do a PhD in the fate and effects of a novel class of pesticide in soil. My first job was as a Government scientist (Department of Agriculture and Fisheries for Scotland) at the Macaulay Institute for Soil Research (now Macaulay Land Use Research Institute) in Aberdeen. I worked on nitrogen cycling in the root zone of cereals with a view to maximising crop uptake via husbandry and reducing the use of synthetic chemical fertilisers. After five years in Aberdeen I became a lecturer in Environmental Science at Thames Polytechnic (now University of Greenwich) in London for two years before moving to work for ICI Agricultural Division at Jealott's Hill Research Station in Berkshire. There I continued to work on nitrogen cycling in soil with a view to providing advice to farmers on how to maximise the amount of applied fertiliser that was taken up by their crops and to minimise the risks of leaching to groundwater.

When ICI sold their fertiliser business to Norsk Hydro, I moved to Shell Research Limited at Sittingbourne to work in team studying the fate and effects of new candidate pesticides in soils to meet legislative registration requirements for new products. When Shell sold their crop protection business to American Cyanamid in 1991, I transferred to the Contaminated Land Group of the Environmental Section of the Oil Products Research & Technical Services (now Shell Global Solutions), based initially at Sittingbourne and then relocated just to the north of Chester in 1995.

The Contaminated Land Group is a multi-centre (Chester, Hague, Houston), multi-disciplinary group of hydrogeologists, engineers, geochemists, modellers, chemists and biologists which provides consultancy to Shell companies worldwide on the investigation, risk assessment and remediation of soil and groundwater contamination. Shell operates in more than 130 countries around the world and we have projects in all five continents. I am the expert on bioremediation within the Group. Besides consultancy work, I am also responsible for our Research and Development (R&D) programme in contaminated land, which is aimed at developing more cost-effective methods of site investigation and remediation. I am also expected to keep the Group abreast of external developments in the subject. To achieve this I am involved with several external Working Groups and Networks. I am Chairman of the Soil and Groundwater Technology Association (SAGTA) and the Advisory Board of the FARADAY Partnership (virtual centre) on Contaminated Land, a Board member and Trustee of CL:AIRE (Contaminated Land: Applications in Real Environments) and a member of the Institute of Petroleum and CONCAWE (European Oil Industry Health and Safety Executive Forum) Taskforces on Soil and Groundwater Contamination."

Bob Harris - Head of National Groundwater and Contaminated Land Centre, Environment Agency (EA)

"I have worked within the UK water industry for the whole of my career. After obtaining a first degree in Chemistry and Geology, I took a one-year Masters degree in Organic Geochemistry. At the time (1972), pollution was just becoming popular and my dissertation looked at the uptake of heavy metals from a sewage works effluent in the sedimented organic matter of a river. Luckily, during a time of job scarcity, this helped me obtain a post within the water industry, firstly as a water supply chemist with a small Water Board and then as commissioning chemist for a big water treatment works in Severn-Trent Regional Water Authority. Seeing an opportunity to specialise in groundwater pollution and its prevention, I took it, since the job related more to my background and interests. I have subsequently worked in this area for the rest of my career.

I think my progression to my current role as Head of the Environment Agency's National Groundwater and Contaminated Land Centre (NGWCLC) has been achieved by a combination of fate (being in the right place at the right time) and an ability to apply experience gained on-site to the wider context within research and policy. The NGWCLC is an expert group providing a focus for those both within and outside the Agency on all the associated technical aspects relating to groundwater resource management, its quality and protection, and contaminated land and groundwater remediation. The Centre has a large programme of applied R&D and technical guidance development and a budget of around £3 million per annum. The work programme is highly focused on the needs of practitioners both in a national (policy) and site specific role and having been engaged at all levels in the same field over a career of 30 years has helped me define it. I try to share experience and practice wherever possible and am an active participant on many national and international groups relating to groundwater, waste disposal and contaminated land issues. Spreading the message internationally and gaining new ideas from others still gives me a buzz in a professional area that has become more exciting in its possibilities with time."

Jim Pritchard - Area Hydrogeologist, Scottish Environment Protection Agency (SEPA)

"The workload of a SEPA Hydrogeologist is diverse, stimulating, and often presents opportunities to make a real contribution to environmental improvement and the promotion of sustainable development. I have worked for SEPA since 1999 and my main tasks have included the provision of advice to SEPA staff on a range of hydrogeological issues such as the assessment of the risks posed to the water environment by landfills, contaminated land sites, mining activities, quarries and new groundwater abstractions. I have also been required to set up and run groundwater monitoring networks in order to satisfy the requirements of legislation such as the EC Nitrates Directive and the EC Groundwater Directive. I have recently taken on the role of Lead Hydrogeologist on the groundwater-related aspects of the Water Framework Directive within SEPA's Operations Directorate. This involves the supervision of the workload of other members of staff to ensure that targets are met, contributing to guidance, project management of R&D and liaison at a UK level to promote a consistent approach.

I graduated from the University of Birmingham with a degree in Chemical Engineering with Minerals Engineering. The minerals aspects of the course sparked an interest in geology, which I then built upon with an MSc in Groundwater Engineering at the University of Newcastle upon Tyne. On completion of my MSc, I joined the Environment Agency where I worked as an Assistant Hydrogeologist in the Shrewsbury office before securing a promotion to the position of Hydrogeologist in the Leeds office. At the Environment Agency my work consisted of groundwater abstraction licensing, local authority planning consultations relating to quarries and opencast coal sites, and landfill regulation. I also ran projects including the design and installation of a network of groundwater monitoring boreholes and an assessment of the rebound of groundwater from abandoned mines in the Yorkshire Coalfields.

Far from leaving the training received during my first degree in Chemical Engineering with Minerals Engineering behind me, I would say that my background has given me a useful combination of skills and knowledge that are of benefit in my work as a hydrogeologist. This is particularly true in terms of the understanding of chemistry that I bring to the assessment of contaminated land sites, for example, or the numeracy skills that are of use in groundwater modelling and other mathematical techniques used in hydrogeology. Hydrogeology is a multi-disciplinary field and many hydrogeologists come from a background of mathematics, chemistry or other disciplines. This often gives them a combination of skills uniquely suited to a particular niche of hydrogeology. There is no standard career path that must be adhered to - if hydrogeology interests you, pursue it."

Mark Morton - Regional Hydrogeologist, Environment Agency (North East Region)

"My job is very broad-based in terms of Hydrogeology. I cover development of national and regional policy and its implementation. I represent the region on national groups both within and beyond the Environment Agency (EA). I am also the regional technical specialist providing support to Area teams on major projects or contentious issues. I also sit on steering committees for various Research and Development (R&D) projects run by the EA. My current job covers a wide range of areas looking at both water resources and water quality and also waste and contaminated land. This broad mix of roles and responsibilities means my job is never dull, if at times a little hectic. In terms of using my technical skills and knowledge it is mainly about looking at the bigger picture and taking a more strategic approach. But, when dealing with specific local issues I still need to apply the fundamentals and principles of geology and hydrogeology to produce workable solutions.

To get to my current job I followed the usual mix of twists and serendipity. An honours degree in Geology with Geochemistry in Manchester was followed by an MSc in Geochemistry at Leeds. An interview just down the road at what was then the National Rivers Authority led to a job in York as a Hydrogeologist. I then moved to provide groundwater support to the abstraction licensing team before becoming a Contaminant Hydrogeologist. Finally I moved to the Regional Hydrogeologist post. There are a number of key aspects to working in hydrogeology. There is the need to maintain a good technical understanding whilst being able to understand of assimilate lots of other information outside the specialism, the ability to communicate to non geologists is crucial and finally the ability to make decisions based on inadequate data is very important."

Contacts

Jobs

www.newscientistjobs.com
www.ends.co.uk
www.jobs.guardian.co.uk
www.defra.gov.uk
www.environment-agency.gov.uk
www.sepa.org
www.ehsni.gov.uk
www.countryside-jobs.com
www.environmentpost.co.uk

General

British Geological Society
Kingsley Dunham Centre, Keyworth, Nottingham, NG12 5GG
Tel: 0115 936 3100
www.bgs.ac.uk

Environment Agency (EA)
HQ: Rio House, Waterside Drive, Aztec West, Almondsbury, Bristol BS32 4UD.
Tel: 01454 624 400.

www.environment-agency.gov.uk

The Geological Society
Burlington House, Piccadilly, London, W1J 0BG
Tel; 020 7434 9944
www.geolsoc.org.uk

International Association of Hydrogeologists
PO Box 9, Kenilworth, Warwickshire, CV8 1JG
www.iah.org

The Scottish Environment Protection Agency (SEPA)
Corporate Office, Erskine Court, Castle Business Park, Stirling, FK9 4TR
Tel: 01786 457700.
www.sepa.org.uk

Specialist in Land Contamination
Institute of Environmental Management and Assessment, St. Nicolas House, 70
Newport, Lincoln, LN1 3DP
Tel: 01522 540069
www.silc.org.uk

Water UK
1 Queen Annes Gate, London, SW1H 9BT
Tel; 020 7344 1827/1811
www.water.org.uk

19. Air Quality & Odour Control

Michael Bull, Arup

The Sector

Air quality has become a major environmental issue due to increasing health concerns and the increasing amount of legislation relating to the sector. The sector involves many different issues but can be readily split into two areas, monitoring and assessment. Odour assessment is essentially a subset of the air quality sector. In general it is an issue that relates to nuisance rather than health concerns but many of the same principles of assessment apply. The air quality sector has experienced a major expansion in recent years and the opportunities available have consequently increased.

Air quality monitoring involves the measurement of the concentrations of pollutants, either at the point of emission from, for instance, an industrial process or vehicle, or in the external atmosphere. There are a number of companies that specialise in industrial process emission measurement as this is often a requirement of the permit to operate the site.

Air quality assessment is the examination of the quality of the atmosphere and its potential change due to a proposed change in an urban or rural area. Although this will use monitoring on occasions to establish a baseline, the assessment process is usually based on the use of modelling methods varying from simple screening procedures to complex computer based software. Within the sector there is the opportunity to examine a wide range of issues and to develop a wide range of skills, including communication, interpretative, reflective, mediation, negotiation, team-working and leadership skills.

Sector Profile

This sector has experienced major growth in the past five years, mainly as a result of new legislation, but also because of an increasing awareness of the health issues. Several hundred experts are employed by local authorities in positions that are largely concerned with air quality issues. Within the consultancy sector there has been similar growth as a result of demand for air quality consultancy services, with potentially 300 to 400 consultants actively involved in air quality issues. Including positions elsewhere within industry, research, national government and academia, this means that some 2000 to 3000 people are involved in air quality issues on a day-to-day basis.

Typical Post Names

Environmental Health Officer, Pollution Control Officer, Environmental Consultant, Environmental Manager, Air Quality Manager

Main Employers

Local Authorities, National Government (including the Scottish Executive and the Environment Agency), Government-funded Research Organisations and Educational Institutions, Environmental Consultancies, Environmental Non-Governmental Organisations (NGOs), Major Business and Industry, Airports

Career Opportunities

There is no nationally recognised 'air quality' qualification, thus people arrive in this field with various backgrounds (see the personal profiles below). In general a numerate degree is required, particularly if concentrating on air quality modelling. Typical degree qualifications are in Environmental Technology/Management, Environmental Sciences, Physics, Chemistry, Chemical Engineering, Meteorology and Civil Engineering.

Within the public sector there are several opportunities with a modest level of experience. As a result of air quality related legislation many urban local authorities employ pollution control officers, whose main roles are air quality related issues and regulation of industrial processes (again largely related to air quality issues). Some authorities use the expertise of their Environmental Health Officers to undertake this role and this is a major route into the air quality area. National Government has a mixture of experience, employing both very specialist scientists to meet particular roles and personnel with a more general background for administrative roles (albeit with a requirement for detailed knowledge of the subject area).

Consultancies look for experience gained within industry, government and academia. Many larger consultancies will recruit graduate personnel and train them in the specialist skills required. However, consultancies particularly look for staff with a second degree at MSc or PhD level.

Entry level salaries in the sector depend on employer, the area and nature of the position. Typical starting salaries are in the range of £18,000 to £20,000 increasing to around £25,000 after a few years of experience. Staff with more than 5 years experience are particularly in demand and can command an enhanced salary package. Employment packages in the non-profit sectors are generally lower but the positions are a valuable way to gain experience of the various issues and to work in an area where you have a personal commitment.

Issues and Trends

Within local government the major driver for air quality related work is the Review and Assessment of air quality required under the Environment Act 1995. Local authorities are expected to undertake a review and assessment of air quality in their area at regular intervals. Where the review suggests that air quality objectives will not be achieved, the authority must develop an Action Plan to improve air quality. This has been a major change in responsibilities for many local authorities and has led to many positions being created in this field. It also means that planning applications are scrutinised to ensure that they do not result in adverse air quality impacts. In addition, local authorities also regulate several industries under the Pollution Prevention and Control Regulations 2000. For the types of processes authorised by local authorities, these are mainly concerned with regulation of atmospheric releases.

The same regulations drive the type of work undertaken by environmental consultants. Some consultancies have specialised in undertaking the Review and Assessments for local authorities whilst others are concerned with industrial clients seeking permits from the Environment Agency or local authority. In general, within a consultancy you can expect exposure to a wider range of project types.

Personal Profiles

Rupert Furness - Department for Environment Food & Rural Affairs (DEFRA)

"I work in the Air and Environment Quality Division of the Department for Environment, Food and Rural Affairs (DEFRA). I head the branch which deals with national and local air quality policy issues. My main responsibilities include co-ordinating reviews of the Air Quality Strategy and overseeing the local air quality management process, as well as ensuring that policies developed elsewhere across Government take proper account of their likely air quality impacts.

I joined the civil service as an administrator on the fast-stream graduate entrant programme in 1992, and since then I have worked in various policy jobs. These included a year working on local government finance policy, and two years working as a desk officer covering UK policy on single market issues in the Cabinet Office's European Secretariat.

I studied Classics at Cambridge University after which I spent 2 years as an English teacher in Greece. I went on to do an MA in modern Greek culture and literature at King's College London.

My advice to anyone considering working in central Government is that the civil service offers a good opportunity for the non-specialist to work in a wide variety of policy jobs. You are given a lot of responsibility at an early stage in your career, and you have to be prepared to be thrown in at the deep end - a degree in Classics is not much help when you are trying to develop policy on standard spending assessments or low emission zones. But the training opportunities and sheer variety of work are very attractive, and working closely with Government Ministers can be very rewarding."

Kirsty Weston - Environmental Scientist, Arup

"I am employed as an Environmental Scientist with Arup Environmental, working within the Environmental Science Group. I am principally responsible for undertaking specialist air quality studies and Environmental Assessment projects. I am an IEMA (Institute of Environmental Management and Assessment) Associate Environmental Auditor.

I qualified with a first degree in Geography from the University of Sheffield and an MSc in Environmental Monitoring and Assessment from Coventry University, during which I undertook a placement at a small environmental consultancy in Leicester. After my MSc I worked for the Leicestershire Waste Minimisation Association for 18 months, assisting businesses to analyse, understand and minimise their waste. During this time I gained the background and experience necessary to register as an Associate Environmental Auditor.

I joined Arup Environmental in November 1999, after approaching them with a speculative letter. I now undertake air quality assessments, dispersion modelling and air quality monitoring. For Environmental Assessment projects I act as the project manager for the study, co-ordinating specialist inputs and assessing the overall significance of the predicted impacts. Additional work includes Phase I Environmental Audits of industrial units, environmental due diligence auditing and desk based auditing/scoping of potential development sites.

My advice to anyone entering the environmental field is to take every opportunity to gain some work experience within the environmental field, at an early stage, as this is a crucial way to give you an 'edge' over other candidates in a highly competitive career field. Don't be afraid to send speculative letters to companies that interest you, as you never know when your CV may land on the right desk at the right time."

Contacts

Department for Environment, Food and Rural Affairs - Air Quality site
www.defra.gov.uk/environment/airquality/index.htm

Encyclopedia of the Atmospheric Environment
www.doc.mmu.ac.uk/aric/eae/english

European Commission
www.europa.eu.int/comm/environment/air

London Air Quality Network
www.erg.kcl.ac.uk/london/asp/home

National Society for Clean Air
www.nsca.org.uk

The Government's own site contains much information on air quality and holds the archive of air quality monitoring data.
www.airquality.co.uk

The Review and Assessment of Air Quality Web Page operated on behalf of the Government
www.uwe.ac.uk/aqm/review

The United States Environmental Protection Agency - detailed resources for air quality
www.epa.gov/ttn

Journals

Air Quality Management (monthly)
Atmospheric Issues Newsletter (bi-monthly)
Clean Air (Technical journal of the National Society for Clean Air)

There are several academic journals concerning air quality issues. Examples are the International Journals of the Science of the Total Environment and Atmospheric Environment.

20. Waste Management

Robin Green, Wardell Armstrong

The Sector

In today's rapidly changing world, creating and operating a sustainable waste management infrastructure presents tremendous challenges and opportunities. Waste Managers deal with everything that Society no longer wants. Total Waste Management Programmes have responsibility for dealing with rubbish arising from industry, commerce and households.

Waste is divided into three main classifications:
- Hazardous or Special waste, which includes all waste that is harmful to human health.
- Municipal waste, which includes ordinary domestic refuse, most food wastes, light industrial and commercial wastes i.e. the contents of the Council dustcart.
- Inert waste, which includes clean earth, and most solid building material.

Historically, Britain's answer for waste was to bury it in landfills. In the UK, we have become very skilled in containing waste in landfills with highly engineered liners, to prevent the products of the waste escaping into the general environment. However, European law will soon (2002) no longer permit the landfilling of untreated waste, apart from inert material, and in order to promote the development of new technologies to treat and dispose of waste, landfilled material is taxed, by the Landfill Tax Levy.

European practice is to rely on a hierarchy of waste treatment. The highest level is waste minimisation - adopting practises to reduce the amount of waste produced to a minimum. Then comes reuse - can the object be used again? If not, can the material be recycled? Recycling depends upon having an acceptable end use for the material. After recycling, the next level to consider is energy reclamation, either as heat, or electricity. At the bottom of the hierarchy is landfill, intended to be the option of last resort.

Sector Profile

Approximately 12,000 people are directly employed in the UK as professionals in the Waste Industry, and the number is increasing rapidly, as the Regulators struggle to administer ever-increasing legislation. The Industry side of Waste Management is growing more slowly, as industry endeavours to become ever more competitive.

Typical Post Names

Environmental Engineer, Environmental Health Officer, Environmental Manager, Environmental Scientist, Environmental Technician, Geologist, Geotechnical Engineer, Site Manager, Minerals and Waste Planner, Scientific Officer, Team Leader - Waste Management, Technical Officer (Waste), Waste Manager, Waste Policy Manager

Main Employers

Environment Agency, Waste Disposal Authorities - County & City Councils, Waste Management Companies (e.g. Biffa, Cleanaway, Onyx, Shanks, SITA, Viridor, Waste

Recycling Group), Non-Governmental Organisations (e.g. Friends of the Earth, Greenpeace), Government Organisations and Funded Institutions, Research Organisations.

Career Opportunities

The sector is divided into three main groups of professionals. These are the Regulators, the Procurers of Services, and the Providers of Services. Non-Governmental Organisations tend to be in the "not-for-profit" sector, and are generally unlikely to have the resources to offer a career structure for young professionals.

The Regulators are the Environment Agency (EA) in England and Wales, and the Scottish Environment Protection Agency (SEPA) in Scotland. Their duties involve the monitoring and inspection of waste facilities to ensure that they are compliant with the licences and permits, and are not causing undue environmental damage. The processing and agreement of licences and permits is also the job of EA/SEPA. A further branch of Regulation is in the hands of the Waste and Minerals Planning Officer in local government, whose job is to ensure that the necessary Waste Management facilities are built at the most acceptable sites. This is normally a County or City Council matter in England. Planning is managed differently in Scotland, where these matters are with the Local Councils. The Environmental Regulators tend to employ graduates with degrees related to their core businesses of Waste, Water, Air, Fisheries, Conservation, Navigation, Recreation and Flood Defence, etc. Formal business qualifications would be expected for those wishing to undertake a managerial role. Formal Training Agreements are sometimes offered.

Procurement of Services is the responsibility of the producer of the waste. Each manufacturing company is responsible for disposing of its own waste, and in many industrial processes this means that extensive treatment of wastes has to be undertaken on site. Waste Services for the public are procured by the Waste Disposal Authorities (normally County, City or local Councils), who contract the necessary facilities. This involves a much wider range of services than collection of domestic waste (the dustcart). It includes the development of a disposal strategy, and the development of a commercial structure, in which a Contractor is paid a price to dispose of all wastes in a way that is publicly acceptable, and which complies with the law. Waste Management work in this sphere is mostly middle management, recruited from other business management streams within the Authority. Minerals and Waste planning is a specific area of Town and Country Planning work.

Providers of the Services are the Waste Management Contractors, who provide and manage facilities which comply with the requirements of the law for the collection, treatment and disposal of wastes. They provide general and specialist transport, collecting waste in a wide range of specially designed vehicles, as well as by barge and by rail. Treatment facilities commonly offered include materials separation, recycling, energy from waste as well as landfill, and also include facilities such as civic amenity sites. Providers employ school leavers, but increasingly recruit university graduates for formal training programmes in technical and scientific skills, and people with business qualifications for managerial positions.

Consultancy services are used primarily by the Service Providers to prepare designs for new facilities, and to prepare formal submissions for permitting purposes. Most provide formal training agreements, leading to formal Professional qualifications.

Graduates in any discipline in science, technology, engineering or humanities may seek to become waste managers, though increasingly a Masters degree in a related subject is advantageous. Waste Management requires a good overall grasp of basic science and technology, both for the protection of flora and fauna in the environment, and for application of technology to reliably achieve waste management whilst exercising that protection. Increasingly, the allied skills of containment and contamination cleanup are also being required.

Salary expectations are comparable throughout the sector. Newly qualified graduates may expect £15,000 to £20,000 per annum, depending on location and discipline, rising to £30,000, for example in the technical grades in the Environment Agency. Private organisations tend to pay a little more for senior technical expertise (perhaps £40,000). Senior Line Management may expect more. Higher-grade management positions, particularly those with significant commercial responsibilities, for example in industry and for contractors, can expect to earn up to £70,000.

Issues and Trends

Energy from Waste: treatments include all heat treatments to recover energy as heat, or convert it to electricity. Whilst there are a number of mass burn incinerators operating in the UK, the lengthy planning process and the requirement to achieve best available technology (BAT) under the latest Prevention, Pollution and Control (PPC) Regulations, mitigates against such plants. Much effort and research is being undertaken into other heat treatments, such as pyrolysis and gasification to extract energy and reduce waste to a minimum volume, whilst minimising gaseous emissions to atmosphere. These are far smaller and cheaper to construct than mass burn incinerators.

Recycling: Whilst being heavily promoted politically, recycling of materials from waste is one of the biggest challenges faced by any modern economy. Britain currently produces more than 400m tonnes of waste each year, and most of this is sent straight to landfill. In its UK Waste Strategies, Government has recognised that this is no longer sustainable, and has set demanding targets to reduce waste and to increase recycling. There is a need to create a continuous demand for recycled products, and to ensure that the demand is fulfilled, by ensuring that at least 15% recycling is achieved across key material streams such as paper, glass and plastics. There is no point in creating mountains of material which cannot be sold.

Materials Recovery: Materials recovery covers the harnessing of the by-products of existing services. The primary example is the reclamation of landfill gas, which includes methane, one of the most powerful greenhouse gases, from existing landfills. A lot of these landfills contain large proportions of biodegradable waste, which, as it decomposes, produces methane and carbon dioxide, the principal constituents of landfill gas. This gas can be collected and used as a fuel. Such fuels may be used for electricity generation, and are a renewable energy resource.

Legislation: Ever increasing environmental legislation is being introduced into the UK from Europe. Whilst most Directives from the EU are necessary, they are not always drafted with due consideration for the practicalities of compliance. It is the Government's obligation to enact regulations to enforce European Directives, and the large number being presented in recent years means that there is a very large number of "Drafts for Consultation" being issued. A number of issues have gone through consultation without achieving workable regulations. For instance, clinical waste was supposed to be collected in 1100 litre yellow "Eurobins" by 1st January 2002. The regulations had to be suspended as there was insufficient industry capacity to make this viable.

Personal Profiles

Judith Harper - Waste Manager, Worcestershire County Council

"I have nearly seventeen years' experience in Waste Management; covering the public sector, private sector, contracting and consultancy.

I graduated from Manchester University in 1984 with a degree in Geology, with specialist options that included hydrogeology. This enabled me to get my first job, as Assistant Waste Disposal Officer at Norfolk County Council. The Council provided me with induction training and on the job training to adapt my academic skills to practical application. Working for a small waste disposal authority provided me with a good grounding in a range of aspects covering the waste industry. In addition I took every opportunity to attend relevant training courses to build up my portfolio and increase my knowledge leading towards an application for Chartered Geologist status, which I gained in 1989.

After three years in local authority I moved to the private sector as Assistant Environmental Engineer at consultants Shanks & McEwan (now Shanks), and was subsequently promoted to Hydrogeologist. I worked for the technical department primarily on site acquisitions (covering design, planning applications and related matters) and on solving hydrgeological problems at existing sites.

After four years I moved to an environmental consultancy, where I undertook mostly the same type of work. At the same time I commenced a management degree (MBA) with the Open University Business School, involving studying in my own time after work and at weekends.

In 1993 I left the consultancy, which was suffering from the downturn in civil and structural engineering. I joined Hereford & Worcester County Council as Waste Manager, with responsibility for contracts, pollution control at closed landfill sites, and recycling/waste minimisation. I initiated a major change in contract arrangements leading to procurement of an integrated waste management contract under the government's private finance initiative (PFI), which I then project managed.

In 1999 I was seconded to central government for 13 months, as policy advisor to Department of the Environment, Transport and the Regions (DETR), to provide a local authority perspective in matters such as the national waste strategy, Best Value and PFI.

Following local government reorganisation I remained with Worcestershire County Council managing the waste management service on behalf of both Herefordshire Council and Worcestershire County Council."

Shaun Trigg - Regional Environmental Manager, Waste Recycling Group

"My career in waste management began, as is often the case, unwittingly, when I joined a local consultancy as a junior environmental technician. The position came about through undertaking a work placement from my college course (BTEC National Diploma in Environmental Science). In the last three months of the course I had secured a part time junior clerical role. This was followed by a position of junior environmental technician once the course was complete.

In the first couple of years I was able to build on good relations with many of the staff which, together with my enthusiastic approach, made for good development of my skills, being able to experience a wide variety of environment related duties.

My employer then supported an application to undertake a correspondence type degree course, BSc Waste and Environmental Management, at De Montfort University, and I become a student member of the Chartered Institution of Wastes Management (CIWM).

As my knowledge grew, I was able to develop my work experience at a similar rate, and by the time I completed the course, I had several years experience of a Scientist/Engineering nature and subsequently became an Environmental Scientist. In addition, I gained full membership of the CIWM, and took up the role of co-ordinator of the New Generation Group in the West Midlands.

After an eight year period, a fresh challenge was needed and after several months enlisted with employment agencies a suitable opportunity was found. I am now employed with Waste Recycling Group, a large waste management operator, as Regional Environment Manager.

The challenge now is ensuring that the next decade is as fruitful as the last."

Mark Haslam - Team Leader, Tactical Planning, Environment Agency

"I graduated from Manchester University in 1988 with a BSc Honours Degree in Biology and Geology, but it was not until 1990 that I embarked upon my career in Waste Regulation and Environmental Protection.

I started on a 2-month temporary contract with West Yorkshire Waste Management based in Brighouse as a Landfill Gas Survey Technician identifying former landfill sites, undertaking desk studies, monitoring sites and analysing and presenting data. The contract was subsequently extended by 6 months and I became more interested in the inspection of sites and investigation of incidents, so when a vacancy arose for an Assistant Waste Regulation Inspector I applied and was taken on as a permanent employee.

Following 18 months in West Yorkshire I applied to Staffordshire County Council and got a job as an Environment Control Officer, based at Stafford. I undertook inspections of authorised and unauthorised waste management sites and began to get involved in assessing applications for waste disposal licences (as they were then). This proved to be a good career move in that the department was under-resourced and required additional staff to implement the new waste management licensing regime, and so in 1992 I gained promotion to Senior Environment Control Officer. This post was a team leader's job with 6 staff involved in waste management site inspections, enforcement investigations and issuing waste management licenses. In 1994 I applied for the post of Principal Environment Control Officer which I held for 3 years. This involved managing 10 staff involved in determining waste management licences, modifications, transfers, surrenders and exemptions. During this period I also had the opportunity to manage the industrial waste survey and write the Staffordshire Waste Management Plan and Annual Reports.

I was transferred to the Environment Agency upon its formation where I continued with a similar line of work but became more involved in waste minimisation and packaging waste. In 1997 following reorganisation I became Team Leader, Tactical Planning, based at Lichfield. This post involved managing 10 staff involved in packaging waste compliance, waste management planning and waste minimisation. In addition it also allowed me to widen my experience into the fields of pollution prevention and water quality sampling and planning. In 2001 I took a nine-month secondment as Team Leader Process Industry Regulation and Radioactive Substance Regulation. This post has involved managing 10 staff in the regulation of processes authorised under Integrated Pollution Control, Integrated Pollution Prevention and Control, Control of Major Accident Hazards and Radioactive Substances. I have also retained an involvement in waste minimisation and packaging waste. The secondment is about to draw to a close and I am looking forward to taking on a new and challenging role, no doubt with at least some involvement in waste regulation."

Contacts

Employers

Biffa
www.biffa.co.uk

Cleanaway
www.cleanaway.com

Environment Agency
www.environment-agency.gov.uk

Local Authorities - Municipal Yearbook
www.knowuk.co.uk/html/about_myb.htm

Onyx
www.onyxgroup.co.uk

Scottish Environment Protection Agency
www.sepa.org.uk

Shanks
www.shanks.co.uk

SITA
www.sitaonline.co.uk

Viridor
www.viridor-waste.co.uk

Waste Recycling Group
www.wrg.co.uk

There are many engineering and environmental consultancies, each offering a different range of services to the market, and the best way to identify those with the particular skill stream sought is to consult a directory such as the International Directory published by CIWEM.

Magazines and Journals

Water and Environment Manager
CIWEM Journal
Wastes Management
Surveyor
Waste Planning
Waste Management World
ENDS (www.ends.co.uk)

Institutions and Forums

Chartered Institution of Wastes Management
www.ciwm.co.uk

Chartered Institution of Water and Environmental Management
www.ciwem.com

Construction Industry Research & Information Association
www.ciria.org.uk

Environmental Services Association
www.esauk.org

EU Directorate General XI
www.europa.eu.int

Friends of the Earth
www.foe.co.uk

Greenpeace
www.greenpeace.org.uk

Institution of Civil Engineers
www.ice.org.uk

Institution of Mining and Metallurgy
www.imm.org.uk

Royal Institution of Chartered Surveyors
www.rics.org.uk

US Environmental Protection Agency
www.epa.gov

Waste and Resources Action Programme
www.wrap.org.uk

21. Environmental Risk Assessment & Modelling

Professor Simon Pollard, Cranfield University

The Sector

The environment sector employs a large and diverse number of modellers, environmental forecasters and risk professionals. Their work focuses on maximising the use of environmental data by using representations of the environment (environmental models) so as to improve decision-making. Professionals working in this field have a range of disciplinary backgrounds (e.g. hydrologists and hydrogeologists, civil engineers, environmental chemists, toxicologists, biologists, geographers, meteorologists and ecologists) and will most likely have supplemented their first degree with a postgraduate qualification. Well developed numeracy skills, powers of logic and a natural inquisitiveness into how environmental systems behave are all important.

Environmental systems are open, complex, harbour substantial uncertainty and can be unpredictable. Environmental modelling attempts to bring a semblance of order to this complexity, so increasing our decision-making power. This might be for assessing the likely impacts of climate change using statistical techniques, assessing the travel time of contaminated groundwater plumes or estimating the potential exposure from trace metals released from an incinerator stack. The output of environmental models may have many uses: industry uses the output of air quality impact assessments to estimate stack heights for new process plants, regulators use estimates of exposure to polluted soils to help determine whether land is contaminated or not and the research community design and interrogate environmental models to help understand better what the key influences are on a system, for example, what the key determinants are to flood risk in a particular location.

Increasingly, environmental modelling is being set within a broader context of environmental risk assessment and risk management. The aim here is to better understand both the likelihood (probability) and the environmental impacts (consequences) of hazards, such as flooding and chemical or pathogen exposure, and to improve the way in which society can manage them. Tools and techniques for risk assessment can be qualitative or quantitative, the more powerful risk tools dealing with probability. Decision makers use the outputs from environmental models and risk assessments, and with other information on social and economic impacts, decide on the best course of action for managing the risk under study.

Sector Profile

The number of modellers and risk specialists employed by the environment sector is difficult to establish because of the range of job titles that are used. However, there is a clear growing trend of employment in the field of modelling and risk assessment as decision-makers attempt to make best use of environmental data. The ENDS directory offers an authoritative review of career prospects and trends, including those in risk assessment within consultancy, and reports a growing demand across the sector for specialist skills. The ENDS careers report can be found at www.endsdirectory.com

Typical Post Names

Modelling Officer, Environmental Scientist, Risk Analyst, Risk Scientist, Hydrologist, Hydrogeologist, Environmental Quality Assessor, Environmental Forecaster, Data Analyst, Water Quality Modeller, Environmental Modeller, Scientific Officer

Main Employers

- Environmental consultancies
- Regulators
- Government Departments and their Agencies e.g. Environment Agency, Scottish Environment Protection Agency (SEPA), Northern Ireland Environment and Heritage Service, Health and Safety Executive, Department for Environment, Food & Rural Affairs (DEFRA), Department for Trade and Industry (DTI), Centre for Environment, Fisheries & Aquaculture Science (CEFAS)
- Government research institutes e.g. Meteorological Office, the British Geological Survey, the Centre for Ecology and Hydrology, the Plymouth Marine Laboratory, the Proudman Oceanographic Laboratory
- University environmental science and engineering departments
- Utility companies (e.g. Thames Water, Innogy)
- Insurance and re-insurance companies
- Chemical process and petrochemical companies with in-house environmental departments (e.g. BP, Shell, Dow)
- Waste management companies

Career Opportunities

Good modellers and risk analysts understand the capabilities and limitations of their models because they are very familiar with the system the model attempts to represent. Most professionals working in this field have a first degree in the physical, engineering or biological sciences and a postgraduate degree in the environmental sciences. Specialists may have PhDs and have undertaken postdoctoral study, though these are rarely essential. A combination of theory and practice is, however, usually regarded as a pre-requisite for employment in this field. Therefore, many modellers and risk analysts have spent early parts of their careers getting 'on the ground' experience of their subject, through site investigation work for contaminated land risk assessments, ecological surveys for ecological modelling, or hydrometry for flood risk modelling.

Through obtaining and interpreting data, the modeller learns the central importance of high quality information and hence the principle of "garbage in - garbage out". By understanding in depth the science upon which the model rests, the expert modeller is able to select tools that are fit for the purpose and that do not over-extend her / his knowledge of the system. Also important is the need to fully understand the needs of the user of the output. They may have different ideas about how powerful the model might be or the level of confidence associated with the output. Risk analysts have a special interest in assessing the uncertainty inherent to environmental systems and using sensitivity analysis to isolate the key "drivers" of risk - so a sound statistical knowledge is important.

The modeller/risk assessor is analytical. They can break down problems into their component parts and re-assemble them, understand where data comes from, its variability and how best it can be used, and think laterally. Early experience in running or developing even simple models can provide these insights and can then help demonstrate to potential employers an aptitude and understanding of the capabilities and limitations of modelling. Knowing how and where environmental models have been used to good effect (e.g. in the designation of groundwater protection zones, in predictions over marine fish stocks and sediment load to the marine environment, in global climate models, and in multimedia fate and transport modelling) will help.

Increasingly, risk analysts work in, and across, multidiscipline teams and often play a pivotal role in collating the contributions of others to inform the analysis and decisions. These professionals need good interpersonal skills and powers of synthesis that allow them to extract risk- or decision-critical information. They may need to elicit expert opinion from others where data is limited or not available, by running 'brainstorming' sessions and be tenacious and happy to challenge perceived opinion.

Salary expectations in the UK for entry-level professionals in this field are typically £14,000 to £18,000, with higher salaries usually reserved for the private sector. With 2 to 3 years' experience after an MSc, one might expect £20,000 to £23,000, and with a PhD, £25,000 or more. As with most careers, obtaining chartered status helps with your career development and many employers are willing to assist their staff along this route. Experienced risk assessment specialists and managers with 10 to 15 years' experience might expect to earn £35,000 to £45,000 and executive managers or technical directors heading up modelling or risk teams might expect to earn more than £50,000. Certain specialists can command considerable salaries in the insurance field, usually where the modelling is associated with the assessment of natural hazards in a commercial setting.

Issues and Trends

'Risk' is a word used everywhere these days. There is a growing recognition of people's perceptions of risk associated with potential hazards such as GM technology, BSE, trace pesticide residues, emissions from landfills, flooding, etc. Alongside understanding what factors influence these societal concerns, we need sound scientific analyses of these problems. There is a growing need, therefore, for risk professionals and modellers within both the private and public sectors.

The private sector is concerned about business continuity and the avoidance of exposure to accidents, liabilities, prosecutions and shut downs that might negatively impact on shareholder value. Managing risk is a core business activity and most companies employ specialist environmental consultants to assist in auditing and assessing their liabilities. Much of this work is qualitative risk assessment and a portion of it quantitative. As a result, there are considerable opportunities for environmental risk assessment professionals in consultancies. They will assess historically contaminated land, construct safety cases for the chemical process sector, support environmental impact assessments of waste management facilities and assist with disposal strategies for radioactive waste. Large pharmaceutical and consumer product companies are also concerned about potential product risks when they design and market new products. Many companies have quite stringent regulatory requirements that require substantial pre-market environmental testing. They employ environmental modellers to assess the environmental fate and transport of new chemicals and their potential human and environmental impacts.

Environmental regulators are concerned with permitting or authorising activities that may impact on the environment. Furthermore, they have an important monitoring role and act as advisers to Government on the state of the environment. As a result these activities draw heavily on environmental modelling and risk assessment. Acceptable levels of discharge are set, conditions placed on an operator to manage the risk, and forecasts created of the future state of the environment under various policy scenarios.

Many non-government organisations (NGOs) also employ specialist technical staff with strong technical backgrounds and research experience in relevant fields. These organisations are more likely to seek issue-based skills (e.g. waste campaigner, toxics adviser etc.) rather than pure modelling or risk expertise, though individuals with such expertise may be employed, from time to time, on a consultancy basis. NGOs may understandably favour candidates with an understanding of the use and communication of science at policy and public level. Many staff in NGOs combine a technical specialism with campaigning interests to offer 'all-round' skills to these organisations and to ensure that campaigns have a sound basis in science.

The environmental consultancy sector is probably the largest employer of modellers and risk professionals. In addition to their own specialist modelling or risk expertise, consultants need excellent project management skills, well-developed written and oral communication abilities and an aptitude for selling ideas and services to existing and new clients. Good consultants are able to define and scope out problems and offer commercially focused solutions that are fit-for-purpose, keeping in mind their customers needs throughout. They tailor their communication methods and styles to the needs of the customer, are able to challenge perceived views and offer innovation as and when required. Consultants undertaking modelling and risk work are employed in a variety of roles e.g. environmental impact assessment, environmental permitting, auditing, divestiture and acquisition, contaminated land assessment and remediation, and the preparation of industrial safety cases. Senior and Principal consultants will often manage teams across a business and will be looking to expand their company's capabilities and client portfolio by offering new modelling or risk products and services.

Increasingly, models and risk software are becoming more user friendly and many desktop packages are now in use that make environmental modelling and risk assessment sometimes deceptively simple. The wide availability of 'turnkey' risk and modelling packages has meant more users, but the fundamental need to understand the system being assessed first hand has not declined. The application of remote sensing and geographical information systems (GIS) is also proving powerful in gathering and manipulating data. Most modern environmental legislation now includes a specific requirement for discharges, abstractors or plant operators to undertake an environmental risk assessment. This will then inform the regulator's decision on their permit. As a result, these skills are likely to become increasingly important in future years.

Personal Profiles

Albania Grosso - Senior Risk Assessment Scientist, Environment Agency

"I am a member of the Environment Agency's National Groundwater and Contaminated Land Centre (NGWCLC). The NGWCLC is involved in research projects covering the fields of water resources, water quality and contaminated land. My primary role is to provide technical guidance and site-specific support to Agency staff on issues of human health and ecological risk assessment. I also provide guidance on the principles of risk assessment as applied to water resources and water quality management. The NGWCLC's work encompasses a wide range of activities including the effects of mass burial for foot and mouth carcasses, remediation technologies and best practice, and modelling the fate and transport of contaminants in groundwater.

I began my University education in a US pre-medical programme, and after three years of toxicology, endocrinology, and microbiology, decided to focus my career in environmental studies. I subsequently trained as an aquatic ecotoxicologist, earning my Masters studying the impact of metal pollution on algae. I then obtained a second Masters in environmental engineering from the University of Illinois, studying the ecotoxicological impacts of urban and agricultural run-off. It wasn't until my first job in a US consultancy firm that I finally applied my human health background to the risk assessment of Superfund sites. After moving to the UK in 1994, I worked in environmental consultancy before joining the Environment Agency. Perhaps the most important lesson I have learned is that risk assessment requires skills in many different areas of environmental work, including toxicology, statistics, scientific methodology and most importantly, mathematics."

Dr David Santillo - Senior Scientist, Greenpeace Research Laboratories, Greenpeace International

"I am a research scientist working in a team of seven at the Greenpeace Research Laboratories, based at the University of Exeter, UK. These laboratories, with a strong focus on environmental chemistry, form the core of the Science Unit employed by Greenpeace International to provide scientific and analytical support to Greenpeace campaigns worldwide. Our role includes conducting research; contributing both to the academic literature and the international resources of Greenpeace; providing advice on a broad range of issues to ensure the activities of Greenpeace are scientifically grounded; and communicating scientific information in the context of policy development in the public arena. Over sixteen years of our existence, we have published the results of our work extensively.

I trained initially as a marine and freshwater biologist, obtaining my degree (1989) and PhD (1993) from the University of London. After a short period of postdoctoral research on the consequences of eutrophication in the Northern Adriatic Sea, I joined the Greenpeace Research Laboratories in 1994. Early projects drew substantially on my research experience, including documenting the threats to water quality in the western lakes of Ireland, though, over the years, I have gained experience and expertise in a broad range of issues of interest to the organisation. There is a steady demand, from both within and outside the NGO community, to apply this knowledge base to policy development at the national and international levels."

Anna Littleboy - Science Integration Manager, UK Nirex

"My career started with a degree in geochemistry from Reading University followed by four years consultancy in the nuclear and water industries - primarily researching the contamination of drinking water. I joined Nirex in 1990 as a hydrogeologist to provide the technical management of field investigations into groundwater flow at potential sites for a radioactive waste facility. I went on to manage a large team of earth scientists undertaking a multimillion pound site investigation programme near Sellafield in Cumbria.

Site investigations require the integration of fieldwork (to acquire data), data interpretation and modelling. It's a fascinating area to work in and provides the basis for a credible risk analysis - we cannot assess future risks if we don't know how the environmental system is behaving now and has evolved in the past. It is important to be clear about the boundaries between site investigations, the underlying research, risk analysis and the decision making process. Many of my publications have been in this area and I am currently undertaking a PhD on risk and decision-making through University College London.

Throughout my career I have worked across the boundaries between conventional disciplines - firstly between field scientists and modellers, and then between geologists and hydrogeologists. In my current role, I co-ordinate an experienced scientific team, looking at the environmental risks of different options for dealing with radioactive waste, and decision makers having to decide what to do for the best. The increasing trend towards consultative decision-making means this is increasingly about making risk assessment more accessible to non-specialists. This is great - it means that I am covering ground that ranges from the communication of science, through the philosophy of modelling, to the way people in society behave. Running through my work is a central concern for the environment and helping to protect the resources it provides."

Dr Richard Crowder - Halcrow

"I specialise in flood risk assessments and the modelling of flood alleviation schemes, flood warning scheme development, water resource problems and water quality risk assessments. As a consulting engineer my workload is varied, and at times unpredictable. We supply a direct service to clients as well as supporting other divisions in project delivery. With respect to flood risk assessments, we are often assessing the risk of flooding at a particular site and may then work with our engineering division to develop mitigation measures. The water quality work I undertake is perhaps the hardest and most interesting bit of my job as it constantly tests my analytical and technical skills. The communication of our findings to clients is often the most important and difficult element of the work as critical management and investment decisions are often made on the basis of our findings.

On route to my current job I undertook a Civil and Structural Engineering degree and was then fortunate to be offered a research position on an EC-funded project based in Holland. I then worked as a Research Assistant on an Environment Agency funded Research and Development (R&D) project in the UK. Later, I took on the role of senior modeller and subsequently Divisional Manager with Bullen Consultants. I decided to study part time for a PhD, which has certainly paid off in the long run. I became chartered with CIWEM and now sit on the Local Branch Committee. Not only does this help me to keep abreast of events and activities in the area of environmental management as a whole, but is also keeps me in touch with friends and professionals in the industry who work for other organisations."

Professor Simon Pollard - Waste Technology, Cranfield University

"I have recently taken up a new Chair in Waste Technology at Cranfield University having spent four years managing the risk section at the Environment Agency's National Centre for Risk Analysis and Options Appraisal, covering flood risk, climate change, radioactive and non-radioactive chemicals and waste. Working across all environmental media and with other risk experts, the team provides the guiding principles for environmental risk assessment and management that result in better environmental decisions. Their work involves preparing technical guidance, conducting Research and Development (R&D) and offering policy advice on the implementation of risk assessment across the Agency's remit. The team has addressed issues such as BSE in the environment, designing the basis for risk-based flood awareness campaigns, assessing residual risks from incinerator ash and designing tools to assess the range of impacts affecting the state of the environment. Increasingly, the work of Government on risk is focussing on issues of risk policy such as how the precautionary principle might be implemented and the social and economic dimensions to environmental risk management.

I trained as a chemist and obtained a PhD in environmental engineering in 1990 in the re-use of industrial wastes. My background has included spells in academia, consultancy and regulation, and I have been fortunate to view risk problems from a variety of perspectives. I first worked as a risk practitioner with Alberta Environment, a Canadian regulator, on their contaminated site programme through a University of Alberta research contract.

Throughout my career, I have found it important to seek a breadth and depth of experience to progress my professional qualifications, and to maintain a network of professional colleagues I can sound ideas off. To a large extent, most environmental challenges can be viewed as 'risk management' problems with the generic principles of risk assessment being applied to any type of environmental hazard. So, in returning to scientific research at Cranfield, I am applying these broader risk principles to the challenges of sustainable waste management".

Professor James Curran - Head of Futures, Scottish Environment Protection Agency (SEPA)

"Certainly more by chance than good planning I'm in a job that I really enjoy. I have a multidisciplinary team that undertakes horizon scanning and seeks out emerging issues, applying risk assessment and scenario planning to identify the ones that might matter. We co-ordinate research on behalf of the organisation, and also develop the SEPA's contribution to sustainable development. Previously I was SEPA's Head of Science, co-ordinating our scientific activities and setting standards and policies across a spectrum of disciplines including chemistry, ecology, hydrology and ecotoxicology.

My career path has followed a random walk. Initially trained in Physics, I was then certain that I wanted to work in the applied sciences. Having always loved meteorology I took a PhD on the dynamics of the atmospheric boundary layer. Following this with a spell designing and installing an automatic weather station on the summit of Cairngorm, I drifted into oceanography and modelling with an environmental regulator. I was really lucky to be allowed to float around within that small organisation - mixing fieldwork with modelling studies and becoming involved in computing, hydrology, engineering, industry inspection and quality management.

The important things I have learnt from my education and various jobs are enthusiasm for new tasks and the confidence to adopt a questioning approach, closely relating this to robust testing of what is workable. The concepts in modelling of calibration, sensitivity testing and validation are universal and, if they become second nature, are invaluable in all walks of life. Modellers are always asked to take on varied tasks, to push techniques to the limit, to provide informed advice or decisions on the basis of inadequate data, and to understand the risks attached. What more could you ask of the ideal employee in any job? But maybe I'm a bit biased..."

Sunita Purushottam - Modeller, Casella Stanger

"I joined Casella Stanger in April 2001 as a consultant. I had heard of Casella in India. I had used their weather monitoring units during some research work. The profile for my job covered a wide range of dispersion modelling work and air pollution monitoring, which fitted my area of interest exactly. I was looking forward to learning the application of Geographical Information Systems (GIS) in air pollution modelling work.

I am currently involved in all types of dispersion modelling work, involving Integrated Pollution Prevention and Control applications, including stack emissions modelling, review and assessments, and development projects involving car parks and road traffic impact modelling.

The variety of the job makes each task very interesting to handle. There is also a lot to look forward to in the future. Its good to be part of a dedicated team and the atmosphere at Casella Stanger is very friendly. Career and technical development is very much encouraged and all team members receive considerable help and guidance from senior colleagues."

Contacts

The web sites and their associated links in the section below offer useful sources of initial information on the application of environmental modelling and environmental risk assessment. Many organisations and professional bodies will happily put serious applicants in touch with their staff or members to talk through potential employment opportunities.

A comprehensive set of contact addresses in this field can be found in the DEFRA / Environment Agency Guidance on Environmental Risk Assessment and Risk Management located at www.defra.gov.uk/environment/eramguide

Centre for Environment, Fisheries & Aquaculture Science
www.cefas.co.uk

Countryside Jobs Service
www.countryside-jobs.com

Department for Environment Food & Rural Affairs
www.defra.gov.uk

Environment Agency
www.environment-agency.gov.uk

Environmental Data Services (ENDS) Journal
www.ends.co.uk

Environment and Heritage Service Northern Ireland
www.ehsni.gov.uk

Environment Post
www.environmentpost.co.uk

Greenpeace Research Laboratories
www.greenpeace.to

Jobs Unlimited
www.jobs.guardian.co.uk

New Scientist
www.newscientistjobs.com

Risk World
www.riskworld.com

Scottish Environment Protection Agency
www.sepa.org.uk

Society for Risk Analysis
www.sra.org / www.sraeurope.org

Further Reading

The Chartered Institution of Water and Environmental Management (CIWEM) has produced 'Risk Assessment for Environmental Professionals', which gives an overview of the practical application of risk assessment in the environment sector.

The texts 'Risk Analysis' by David Vose (John Wiley); 'Environmental Risk Assessment' produced by the European Environment Agency; and 'Environmental Modeling: Fate and Transport of Pollutants in Water, Air and Soil' by Jerry Schnoor (John Wiley) are all useful introductory technical material.

22. Environmental Impact Assessment & Auditing

Tom Matthewson, Binnie Black & Veatch

The Sector

Environmental Impact Assessment (EIA) is the process by which the impacts of a proposed development are assessed and measures identified that will reduce these impacts to an acceptable level. Being development driven, EIAs are usually undertaken by commercial consultancies, employing holistic teams that include generalists who manage the production of the EIA but are supported by a range of specialists in areas such as ecology, air and noise pollution, traffic and water quality. In the UK, the demand for EIA services is driven by European and UK legislation. Project work overseas is also driven by a combination of in-country legislation and, in developing countries, the demands of funding/donor agencies. Major infrastructure developments routinely require an EIA as part of the conditions upon which funds are released.

Environmental auditing is partly driven by the need for companies to achieve and maintain compliance with environmental management system (EMS) standards such as ISO14001 or EMAS (Eco-Management and Audit Scheme). EMS specialists and auditors can work for companies operating an EMS, consultancies offering advice on EMS implementation or for the certification bodies that verify whether a company's EMS meets one of the recognised standards. Increasingly, EMS specialists are also expected to work in other related areas such as health and safety and quality management systems, corporate reporting and expanding EMSs to address the wider issues of sustainable development.

Auditors are also often required as part of 'due diligence' exercises during major mergers and acquisitions. The rewards in this sector can be substantial, as environmental managers often work with multinational corporations who expect the very highest standard of expertise.

Sector Profile

By its diverse nature it is hard to be precise about the number of individuals employed in EIA and auditing. Commercial consultancy forms the single largest recruiting sector for environmental specialists, probably accounting for at least half of those involved in EIA and auditing. It is anticipated that there will be a continued demand for professionals in these areas.

Typical Post Names

EIA Scientist, EIA Consultant, Environmental Consultant, Environmental Assessor, EIA and Policy Consultant, Ecological Consultant, EIA Project Manager, EIA Co-ordinator, Environmental Scientist, Environmental Planner

Main Employers

Engineering and environmental consultancies with in-house EIA, audit and EMS teams

- Major developers with in-house EIA teams
- Certification companies e.g. British Standards Institute, SGS Yarsley, Lloyds Register Quality Assurance
- Donor and lending agencies e.g. Department for International Development (DFID), World Bank
- Regulators e.g. Environment Agency (EA), Scottish Environment Protection Agency (SEPA), Department for Environment, Food & Rural Affairs (DEFRA)
- County and District/Borough Councils

Career Opportunities

Degree-level education, usually in environmental science or related disciplines such as ecology and oceanology will normally be taken for granted by most prospective employers. A post-graduate qualification that provides a higher level of expertise in areas such as environmental management, contaminated land, environmental/process engineering, geotechnics, Integrated Pollution Prevention and Control (IPPC) and audit is also increasingly seen as a mandatory requirement.

Commercial consultancies tend to find experienced graduates much more attractive than those straight from University, and to gain a toe-hold in the profession many graduates find it helpful to undertake some work experience as part of their degree course.

Membership of a professional body such as the Chartered Institution of Water and Environmental Management or the Institute of Environmental Management and Assessment is likely to be increasingly desirable as the environmental services market matures. The Environment Agency is among several organisations having a clear preference for staff to be members of chartered institutions such as CIWEM.

Indicative salaries that can be expected, depending on grade and experience are:
- Public sector: £13,000 rising to £40,000
- Private sector: £15,000 rising to £45,000

Issues and Trends

Whilst the 1999 EU EIA Directive and consequent UK legislation updated the requirements for EIA, as a process it has been undertaken in the UK for at least two decades. Being closely linked to development, the market trend will reflect the state of the general economy and also the level of public investment. Consultancies involved in EIA tend to try and balance the risks involved by seeking a broad portfolio of clients both in the UK and overseas, with the result that a varied and interesting career is often on offer.

Auditing went through a more recent career boom in the 1990s, linked to the adoption of formalised EMS approaches by many major UK businesses. This trend has not continued at quite the same level in recent years but it is considered to remain a strong area for growth as small and medium sized businesses adopt Environmental Management Systems.

There is concern that these sectors have been through a boom period in recent years and that a period of job-shedding is inevitable, especially if the UK economy enters a recession. However, the majority of EIA and auditing work is driven by legislation rather than economics and therefore is to some extent insulated from external fiscal drivers.

More significant employment growth in the sector is likely to come from the emergence of new specialisms, such as those relating to sustainability, climate change and carbon trading.

Personal Profiles

Alvin Smith - Water Scientist, Binnie Black & Veatch

"I am a water scientist with a multidisciplinary engineering consultancy who specialise in water industry projects. Initially concerned with the untoward effects that biological agents have on engineering objectives, I have in later years become far more involved with reducing the effects of man-made schemes on the environment. I have been responsible for a large number of environmental assessments of projects, particularly water supply and sanitation schemes in the UK and overseas including evaluation of strategic environmental impacts for master-plans in developing countries.

My first appointment was to study the potential problems caused by plants and animals of a marine embayment once the area had been barraged and river water stored in the bay. I thoroughly enjoyed designing my own laboratory and boat facilities and setting up and running the comprehensive benthic, planktonic and fishery surveys. Had I but known it, I was carrying out a pre-construction baseline survey, 20 years before those terms came into common use! The objective was to determine the implications, and to develop plans for, the management of the freshwater life that would develop once the barrage was built. The main concerns were to avoid excessive growth of water weeds and algae due to eutrophication. A range of indigenous Chinese carp were introduced to the new reservoir which rapidly became established.

I have subsequently been responsible for the water quality, ecological and environmental issues arising from Binnie Black & Veatch's projects over the past 30 years. During this time, I have worked closely with a wide range of engineering and planning disciplines on infrastructure and capital structure schemes ranging from water supply and natural resource management schemes to industrial effluent discharges.

I enjoy the involvement with design teams to ensure that environmental issues and constraints are taken into account from the inception of the project and that the Best Practicable Environmental Option is adopted. I have specified, commissioned and set up investigative or routine monitoring surveys of marine and freshwater ecosystems for baseline, construction period and post project surveys. Surveys undertaken have included coastal and inter-tidal habitats for flora and fauna, mammal and bird population assessments, fish and shell-fishery yield estimates. Limnological surveys in rivers and lakes have included physical mixing assessment and water quality and invertebrate animal sampling, algae and bacteriological sampling, spot and automated water sampling from surface and depths. Studies of coastal habitats have included false colour infra red photographic aerial surveys with ground control botanical surveys, rain forest, wetland and grassland vegetation surveys.

I have served as member, Secretary and Chairman of the Environment Group of the Chartered Institution of Water and Environmental Management (CIWEM) and am currently a member of Council of CIWEM."

Julia Pinnington - Ministry of Defence

"I graduated in Environmental Biology and Environmental Science from Oxford Brookes University in 1993 and have since specialised in environmental impact assessment, ecology and planning projects.

My first job after graduating was with a firm of environmental consultants (a public company listed on the stock exchange). I provided environmental advice to property developers and government departments on housing, roads, business parks, urban and rural development projects. Here I gained experience on a wide range of environmental issues, office management and communication skills. It was a fast moving, exciting but pressurised place to work, and rewarding if you thrive on working as part of a team to tight deadlines.

Since then I have moved to work with the Ministry of Defence (MoD), a complete contrast. I still provide advice (i.e. ecology, environmental assessment projects, environmental legislation, land use and landscape) but also get involved with designing management plans for the MoD's estate, habitats and species. I work alongside the military personnel and provide day to day advice on a wide range of issues. My role also includes developing national environmental strategy and policy for the Army and liaison with national and local organisations such as The Ramblers Association or National Parks. The work is very different from consultancy and has a strong policy, management and political element. I would recommend it to anyone wanting to manage people, with an interest in politics and those who can think on their feet to answer wide ranging queries.

I am a chartered Biologist and a member of the Institute of Biology, I am also an associate member of the Institute of Environmental Management and Assessment (IEMA)."

Matt Klein - Binnie Black & Veatch

"I have a background in marine ecology and environmental science with degrees from the University of Auckland, New Zealand. For my Masters, I was based at the University of Auckland's marine laboratory where I investigated the use of environmental indicators in the intertidal marine environment. Since leaving university in 1994, I have been employed as an environmental consultant in private practice, both in New Zealand and in the United Kingdom.

My first job was with a company that is now called Meritec. Meritec is a large multidisciplinary engineering consultancy, which was involved in a wide range of traditional engineering projects within New Zealand and South-east Asia. This role enabled me to gain a practical understanding of how large infrastructure projects develop from inception to completion. Following this, I worked at Mitchell Partnerships, a specialised environmental consultancy. Being part of a smaller team of enthusiastic environmental professionals working on New Zealand's most controversial resource use projects was exciting and challenging.

I joined Binnie Black & Veatch soon after arriving in the United Kingdom and am employed as a senior environmental scientist. In this role, I work on strategic environmental management projects, principally flood defence strategies prepared on behalf of the Environment Agency. This involves preparation of Strategic Environmental Assessments (SEAs), communication plans, risk assessments, stakeholder consultation and client liaison. The opportunity to work within two different statutory regimes provides an interesting opportunity to compare and contrast the strengths and weaknesses of each.

In my role as an environmental consultant, I have undertaken several Environmental Impact Assessments (EIAs) and conducted environmental due diligence for a range of mergers and acquisitions. I have mainly been involved with large natural resource use projects, including flood defence schemes, hydro-electricity dams, gold mining, sewage treatment plants, waste management projects, timber processing plants, pulp and paper mills, and very large aquaculture (marine farm) projects. The most interesting parts of my job are being able to work with industry to achieve environmental improvements, and interacting with people who have different viewpoints. It is satisfying when consensus on environmental issues can be reached, but this is not always the case!

The role of environmental consultant is challenging and I would encourage new graduates to become part of this exciting and dynamic industry."

Nicola Whittle - Regional EIA Co-ordinator, Environment Agency

"I graduated from Birmingham University in 1993 with a BSc Hons. degree in Geography. I started work with the Environment Agency in 1994 and have worked my way up through the organisation from Technical Assistant, based in an area office in Dorset, South West Region, to Regional EIA Co-ordinator, based in Reading, Thames Region.

I have worked in multifunctional departments, including the Planning Liaison department where I responded to Local Authorities on statutory planning consultations and liased with developers and the public, the Local Environment Agency Plans (LEAPs) department where I wrote LEAPs, which are catchment based action plans, and was involved in educational and environmental partnership projects. Since 1999 I have specialised in Environmental Impact Assessment.

I worked as an Environmental Impact Assessment (EIA) Officer for a year assessing the environmental impact of Environment Agency works and activities to ensure compliance with EIA and other environmental legislation. The work involved carrying out, and managing external consultants to carry out, EIAs for various projects including Flood Alleviation Schemes, weirs, locks and gauging stations. Liaison with Environment Agency functional specialists, external organisations and the public was a key element of the job to ensure that works were designed and constructed in a sustainable way, minimising environmental impact and maximising environmental enhancement.

I now have a more strategic role, as the Regional EIA Co-ordinator, managing a team of six EIA Officers. The job involves team management skills such as daily and longer term workload management and business planning, staff appraisals, development and training and budget management, and includes national involvement in developing EIA and Strategic Environmental Assessment (SEA) policy and procedures. I am a member of the Chartered Institution of Water and Environmental Management (CIWEM)."

Paul Jackson - Arup

"I have worked in environmental consultancy for six years after graduating from Lancaster University with a degree in Environmental Sciences. I specialise in environmental auditing and environmental management and am a member of IEMA and an IEMA Registered Environmental Auditor.

My main area of experience is in due diligence work, and I have undertaken numerous due diligence audits across a range of industry sectors. I act as a lead auditor and am also involved in project management of due diligence work; this involves co-ordinating site audits and further investigation both in the UK and internationally, and reporting back to the client on key environmental liabilities and risks that could affect the deal.

I work closely with manufacturing companies and other industrial clients, and have advised a number of companies on implementing an EMS to achieve certification to the international standard ISO14001. This has included undertaking initial environmental reviews, developing systems and procedures, providing training and auditing of environmental performance.

I have also undertaken preliminary environmental assessments for major infrastructure schemes, normally at feasibility stage or in support of planning applications. These tend to involve desk-study work to identify key environmental constraints to the development, with co-ordination of specialist surveys such as ecological habitat surveys or archaeology investigation where the desk study has identified particular issues of concern. These preliminary environmental assessments may then go on to full EIA if the project progresses further.

Additional project experience includes writing publications and policy documents for Government departments and agencies in relation to EMS, sustainable development and environmental best practice.

Although based mainly in the UK, my work has also taken me overseas, including France, Greece and Poland."

Contacts

Chartered Institute of Water and Environmental Management
www.ciwem.com

Countryside Council for Wales
www.ccw.gov.uk

Department of Environment, Food and Rural Affairs
www.defra.gov.uk

Department of Trade and Industry
www.habitats-directive.org

Department for Transport
www.dft.gov.uk

Environmental Data Interactive Exchange
www.edie.net

EIA Centre
www.art.man.ac.uk/EIA

Environmental Data Services
www.ends.co.uk

English Nature
www.english-nature.gov.uk

Environment Agency
www.environment-agency.gov.uk

European Environment Agency
www.eea.eu.int

European Environmental Bureau
www.eeb.org

European Information Network
www.eins.org

European Union On-line
www.europa.eu.int

Her Majesty's Stationery Office (www.hmso.gov.uk)

IISD Linkage (www.iisd.ca/linkages)

Information for Local Government
www.info4local.gov.uk

Institute of Ecology and Environmental Management
www.ieem.org.uk

Institute of Environmental Management and Assessment
www.iema.net

National Assembly for Wales
www.wales.gov.uk

Scottish Environment Protection Agency
www.sepa.org.uk

Scottish Natural Heritage
www.snh.org.uk

UK Online
www.ukonline.gov.uk

United Nations Environment Programme
www.unep.org

23. Geographical Information Systems (GIS) & Mapping

Louise Clark, Binnie Black & Veatch

We would like to thank Alan Carnell of Concurrent Appointments who contributed to this chapter.

The Sector

Geographical Information Systems (GIS) represents the most ubiquitous and versatile strand of IT (Information Technology). Many definitions and interpretations of what a GIS is can be found in the literature and promotional material advertising GIS software. A definition by the UK's Department of the Environment (1997) suggests that Geographical Information Systems are:

> *"integrated computer systems for capturing, storing, checking, analysing and displaying data which are geographically referenced to the earth's surface"*

More generally, a GIS is taken to include the operating personnel and the data that go into the system. GIS has become an integral decision-making tool in many businesses and government organisations. The main areas of GIS activity can be categorised as:

· mature technologies which interact with GIS, sharing its technology and creating data for it e.g. surveying, engineering, cartography and remote sensing;

· management and decision-making e.g. resource inventory and management, urban planning (Urban Information Systems), land records for taxation and ownership control (Land Information Systems), facilities management, marketing and retail planning, vehicle routing and scheduling;

· science and research activities at universities and government labs.

Sector Profile

Estimating the size of the GIS market is probably more 'art' than 'science' due to its diversity and varied application across many markets. It is equally difficult to be precise about the number of individuals employed in the GIS and mapping field, particularly as GIS application development moves into the mainstream IT world. However, there is little doubt that the GIS jobs market has recently witnessed rapid growth in its size and diversity. ESRI, the largest GIS software and solution vendor employs 2,500 people worldwide; their main competitor, MapInfo, employs 600.

Typical Post Names

· Catastrophe/Hazard Data Modeller
· Data Capture Operator
· Digitising Technician
· Geodata Technician
· Geodetics Specialist/Engineer/Technician
· Geomatics Engineer/Technician
· GeoInformation Technology Consultant
· Geomatician

- GIS Specialist/Consultant/Professional/Assistant/Officer/ Technician
- GIS Analyst/Programmer
- Gravity Modeller
- Location Based Services Analyst
- Site Location Planner
- Spatial Data Analyst

Main Employers

- Software Houses
- Local and Central Government
- Government Agencies
- Environmental & Engineering consultancies
- Specialist Mapping and GIS consultancies
- Ordnance Survey
- Environment Agency

Career Opportunities

GIS careers fall into two broad areas: those concerned with the data, its analysis and presentation (GIS Analyst); and those concerned with the software and hardware (GIS Application Developer). While they are not mutually exclusive (see Personal Profiles), as GIS software development moves into the mainstream it is likely that the divide between *GIS users* and *GIS application developers* will widen.

The water and environmental information industries lend themselves well to locational referencing and present a stimulating career path to suitably qualified individuals. GIS tools are used extensively within these industries to record, analyse and display attribute data. For example, a GIS loaded with suitable digitised data can work out the likely course of an oil spillage using weather, tidal and oil type data and display its impact in several different contexts such as impact on local wildlife or tourism, including beach contamination.

Most candidates for these positions hold a degree qualification. Geography is the most popular springboard, and in most universities the Department of Geography runs a Masters Degree course in GIS or Geomatics. That said, a first or second degree qualification in Environmental Engineering, Hydrology, Surveying, Civil Engineering, Maths or Computer Science is equally, if not more, relevant to the GIS industry.

If you are of a technical persuasion, experience in applications programming using the currently popular languages of Visual Basic, Java or C++ is very useful. GIS is increasingly seen as an enabling technology for companies' IT systems, so the ability to design, program and implement application software is beneficial. GIS is a database technology so experience gained in MS Access, Oracle or SQL Server software will also enhance your marketability. In recent years Oracle and Microsoft have made significant investment in adding spatial information handling capability to their products, a good indicator of how strategically important this discipline is. Data Analysis and Modelling requires strong statistical skills and experience in software such as SAS, SPSS or MS Excel.

If you are just not cut out for systems and programming, consider a user-centred role where you are the in-house GIS expert on packages such as MapInfo, or ArcView. You need to be a "people-person" for this type of role as clear communication skills are essential in helping your users make maximum use of what can be a complex and difficult to use application.

How much you will earn with your GIS skills and qualifications is down to the type of work you choose and whether you opt for the public or private sector. The private sector would typically offer a starting salary of between £13,000 to £15,000 for a BSc graduate and £15,000 to £18,000 for an MSc graduate in GIS. The public sector often suffers a lack of long term funding, so many jobs in this arena are not permanent but are instead of a fixed term or rolling contract nature, often terminating inconclusively when the money runs out. Generally speaking, GIS jobs in the public domain are less well paid, but this is often compensated by the work being more interesting and having fewer work pressures.

Issues and Trends

The main trend is the increased use of GIS in all industries to improve efficiency and decision-making. For example, there has been considerable growth within the utilities industries and local government in employing GIS to manage assets and data. This trend is likely to widen as GIS moves into computer mainstream and is increasingly accessible from the desktop. The more accessible GIS has become, the more people have wanted it to exist seamlessly as part of the growing global IT infrastructure. With the advent of component GIS, developers can insert a fully functional GIS map into a variety of other applications, using standard languages such as Visual Basic, and enable it to interact directly with other broader business processes.

Employers will be seeking to empower departments and individuals with the tools to share, visualise and analyse GIS data from all parts of the organisation. It is expected therefore that applications will be more market focused and concentrate on specific mapping tasks, rather than providing a wide range of unused functionality - users will become increasingly unaware that they are using mapping technologies. Microsoft is intending to issue its own mapping product, a sure sign of a trend towards wider GIS use.

Web-enabled GIS components are further changing the way in which GIS solutions are delivered. The internet has grown as a delivery platform for geographical data as it provides cost effective implementation to every desktop and to the public. Large amounts of data are now available and accessible via the internet. Binnie Black & Veatch has recently published maps on the Countryside Agency website on behalf of the Countryside Agency. This is a first in many respects, not least the first use of electronic maps for statutory consultation. Projects such as this are helping to open up the GIS community to the potential and benefits of data sharing.

The expense of data is creating a growth market in itself. The generation of data from new sources is an ongoing development. Data standards (OpenGIS) and formats (GML, XML) are under intense debate, as is access to shared data and the issue of Intellectual Property Rights/data ownership.

The increased reliance on data in these systems has brought the emphasis of GIS towards data quality and accuracy rather than mere acquisition - getting and maintaining data is still the most important element of a successful GIS and the most expensive. This is being caused by changing uses of GIS technology and the growth of digital navigation systems (in car, WAP etc) which rely on accurate geographic data in order to function. The growth of positioning and navigation systems has increased the use of Global Positioning Systems (GPS) and remote sensing in the acquisition stage to improve quality. An example is the Ordnance Survey switch from measuring height in terms of datum benchmarks, to using GPS readings.

Personal Profiles

Ian Bush - Technical Director, Binnie Black & Veatch

"My qualifications include a Diploma in Geographical Techniques (Cartography) and an MSc in Construction Information Technology. Initially trained in cartography, I spent 12 years as a land and hydrographic surveyor in the UK and overseas, before moving into geospatial computer technologies in 1989. I was part of an American Aid team that carried out the Land Titling and Registration Project on St. Lucia, where I was responsible for mapping land parcels and settling disputes.

In 1989, I moved to Binnie Black and Veatch (BBV) with the specific brief to set up a department capable of offering an advanced GIS, computer aided design and visualisation service using the latest computer technology, to both internal and external clients. The success of the latter has extended the services offered to the application development of management information systems (MIS), particularly those with a geospatial component.

At BBV, I have been developing and promoting MIS and GIS applications. I have successfully demonstrated on a number of projects that the proper and appropriate use of GIS and associated computer tools can provide effective and efficient support to hydro-environmental engineering and associated business goals. MIS/GIS applications for which I have been responsible include utilities asset management and information systems, water quality and flood modelling, dredging management, sludge-to-land management, shoreline management, risk analysis, and asset management of flood defences. I am now responsible for the technical direction of the Information Solutions Group at BBV and am leading the technical co-ordination on the 'Open Access' mapping project for the Countryside Agency."

Chris Bolam - Senior GIS Applications Developer, Binnie Black & Veatch

"After graduating with a BSc in Environmental Science and Geography and an MA in Geographical Information Systems, I went to work for the Planning Directorate of Kent County Council as a Senior Research Officer. Having developed GIS tools to assist the Planning Department, I then moved to a software house in Kent, where I wrote bespoke GIS components for their suite of environmental asset management products.

At BBV, I head the team of GIS developers, and work on a wide variety of projects, using everything from proprietary and component GIS to web based GIS. I am also responsible for providing technical support and liaison to clients who use the applications BBV has produced. In a current national project, I have designed and produced the Desktop Access Management System for the Countryside Agency. This system allows the client to view and analyse the data that BBV has captured as part of its contract to map 'Open Country' in England. It is my responsibility to support and maintain the application as well as the IT hardware located at the client's offices."

Jonathan Stokes - Senior GIS Analyst, Binnie Black & Veatch

"At university I gained a BSc in Geography and Topographic Science and a Master of Research in the Built Environment, for which my thesis topic was the use and development of GIS for road traffic noise pollution mapping. My first work in the industry started with the product development and maintenance team at Geoplan. This was primarily a research and development role but with a strong emphasis on support for other teams within the company. My role was to update digital and paper mapping products, and to review, design and document update processes of digital datasets from a wide range of sources. I was also involved in the design and creation of update utilities and the design and manufacture of new products.

At BBV, I am currently co-ordinating the mapping team in a GIS and public consultation project for the Countryside Agency, analysing and mapping open country in the UK. I am also working as a consultation officer on the project, liasing with various stakeholders as well as members of the public to provide answers to technical mapping questions. I have also managed the GIS input into environmental management projects carried out by BBV such as flood risk mapping, design of flood alleviation and flood defence strategies."

Lisa Collings - Junior GIS Analyst, Binnie Black & Veatch

"I was introduced to GIS and the variety of its applications during my BSc degree in Geography. I built on this knowledge by studying for an MSc in Remote Sensing, where I found GIS to be a powerful tool for a wide range of environmental applications and a natural partner to remote sensing. Having carried out GIS-orientated work for Sheffield University, I became interested in following an environmental yet technical career, GIS being an obvious choice.

I started employment at BBV in February 2002 as a Junior GIS Analyst. I am working on a wide variety of projects including flood disaster modelling, and flood alleviation and flood defence studies. I am looking forward to developing my skills with the possibility of entering an advisory role to help others use GIS."

Contacts

Software Companies

Autodesk
Tel: 01483 462600
www.autodesk.co.uk

Cadcorp Ltd
Tel: 01438 747996
www.cadcorp.com

eMapSite
Tel: 0118 973 6883
E-mail: info@emapsite.com,

www.emapsite.com

ER Mapper
Tel: 01784 430691
www.ermapper.com

ESRI UK
Tel: 01296 745500
E-mail: info@esriuk.com
www.esriuk.com

Intergraph UK
www.intergraph.com/uk/

Mapinfo
Tel: 01753 848200
E-mail: europe@mapinfo.com
www.mapinfo.com

Other Companies

Ordnance Survey
Tel: 08456 050505
E-mail: enquiries@ordsvy.gov.uk
www.ordsvy.gov.uk

Institutions

Association for Geographical Information
www.agi.org.uk

Geospatial Information and Technology Associates
www.gia.org

Open GIS Consortium
www.opengis.org/

Royal Geographical Society
E-mail: info@rgs.org
www.rgs.org

Journals

AGI resource list
www.geo.ed.ac.uk/home/giswww.html

Geo Connexion
www.geoconnexion.com/

Geo Europe
www.geoplace.com/default.asp

GI News
www.ginews.co.uk

General Journal Lists

Directions Magazine
www.directionsmag.com

Fogler Library
www.library.umaine.edu/sec/guides/gisjournals.htm

Geo Informatics
www.geoinformatics.com

GISnet Online
www.gisnet.com/notebook/giszine.htm

Internet Resources

Department for Environment, Food and Rural Affairs (DEFRA)
www.defra.gov.uk

English Nature
www.english-nature.org.uk

Environment Agency
www.environment-agency.gov.uk

General

GISPortal.com
www.gisportal.com

GIS Development
www.gisdevelopment.net

Geo Community
www.geocomm.com

Employment

Government/Civil Service
www.civil-service.gov.uk/jobs

Local Government
www.lgjobs.com/

General

Concurrent Appointments International
www.concurrent-appointments.com

Earthworks
www.earthworks-jobs.com/

GISjobs.com
www.gisjobs.com

GISL International Consultants
www.gisl.co.uk/jobs.htm

Mailbase
www.mailbase.ac.uk

Universities

University of Greenwich (Dept. of Earth & Environmental Sciences)
www.gre.ac.uk/directory/earthsci/gis-html/gis-links.html

Edinburgh University
www.geo.ed.ac.uk/home/gishome.html

Leicester University
www.geog.le.ac.uk/cti/gis.html

Sheffield University
www.gis.sheffield.ac.uk

University College London
www.ucl.com

References

Department of the Environment (1987) *Handling Geographic Information: The Report of the Committee of Inquiry Chaired by Lord Chorley*, London: HMSO.

24. Energy

David Acres, TXU Energy

The Sector

The energy industry provides electricity, heat and fuel to meet society's energy needs. The sector's activities are very wide ranging and include:
- extracting, refining and distributing fossil fuels, such as coal, oil and natural gas
- operating power stations and distribution networks to supply electricity
- developing new sources of energy, such as wind energy and solar power
- finding new ways to reduce energy demand, including more efficient technologies

A reliable and cost-effective energy supply is vital for industry, for the transport that we use, and for all our domestic needs. However, all forms of energy production have environmental impacts. One of the major challenges facing modern civilisation is to find sustainable and secure ways of meeting our energy needs that do not produce unacceptable environmental consequences.

Sector Profile

The energy sector employs several hundred thousand people in the UK. It forms a substantial proportion of the overall economy - for example, the electricity supply industry alone contributes over 1% of the total UK Gross Domestic Product. Although energy demands continue to grow, in recent years the energy sector has made overall reductions in the number of people employed, due to factors such as the privatisation of the electricity industry. However, in some emerging disciplines, such as environment, employment prospects are stable or improving.

Typical Post Names

Environmental Manager, Environment Agency Inspector, Air Dispersion Modeller, Energy Efficiency Auditor, Environmental Planner, Emissions Monitoring Specialist, Environmental Management System Auditor, Power Station Chemist, Combustion Engineer, Process Engineer.

Main Employers

Environment Agency, Electricity Supply companies (e.g. TXU Energy, Innogy, PowerGen, British Energy, Scottish Power) National Grid, Oil and Gas companies (e.g. Centrica, Shell, BP, Texaco).

Career Opportunities

Public Sector
The main public sector environmental employer is the Environment Agency, which regulates many of the processes and installations in the sector (e.g. power stations, oil refineries). The Environment Agency recruits at many levels, including graduates. Direct experience of the sector will always be helpful, but may not be essential.

Private Sector
Individuals who work on environmental issues for private companies in the energy sector have often specialised in both environment and energy at an early stage. Some have developed their environmental career from a position that included some environmental responsibilities: such transfers remain a common career route within the sector. Others join companies with a higher degree in a relevant environmental specialism (typically a PhD) to work directly on a specific environmental issue. Some of the larger energy companies offer graduate programmes: graduate recruits are expected to gain experience in the wider activities of the company, as well as developing their environmental expertise.

Environmental specialists are not limited to those with qualifications in pure environmental science or environmental management however. For example, a major task for the sector is developing new infrastructure - environmental planners and legal specialists play a key role in obtaining the necessary consents.

The main opportunity for environmental career progression in private companies is providing strategic advice to the organisation. The energy sector is increasingly driven by the environmental agenda and companies need expert advice on how they should plan to meet future constraints. All the larger energy companies employ environmental experts at a senior management level. These individuals have generally combined an initial technical environmental role with a wider understanding of business.

An increasing trend is that many of the environmental specialists working for energy companies are employed from external environmental consultancies, to tackle specific technical issues. This career pathway may be more flexible than working directly for an energy company, as it can involve gaining and applying environmental knowledge and skills that are not specific to just the energy sector. The larger environmental consultancies recruit at all levels of experience, including graduates.

Non Profit Sector
There are a number of non-profit organisations that deal with environmental issues in the energy sector. These include charitable bodies promoting energy efficiency and renewable energy sources. Environmental specialists in these organisations tend to have many years of previous environmental and energy experience, but there are occasional openings for less experienced individuals.

Reflecting the varied environmental career pathways in energy, the range of potentially useful qualifications is wide. A degree or postgraduate qualification in an environmental subject is a good starting point, but the degree will need a strong emphasis on industrial environmental management to attract a private sector employer. A degree in a subject relevant to an aspect of the energy supply process can also provide an entry point into a role that includes some environmental work. Related subjects can include engineering (particularly chemical, process and mechanical), geology, planning, applied chemistry and applied physics.

In addition to academic qualifications, membership of any of the main professional institutions is a useful means of demonstrating the ability to apply knowledge and skills to solve real life problems.

Salaries reflect experience and responsibility and are generally comparable to other employees at a similar level within the organisation, or within other specialist disciplines in the sector. At the top of the scale, an environmental director focusing on environmental corporate strategy could expect a salary in line with any other company director. An environmental specialist with a PhD working on a particular technical issue would have a salary comparable to scientists working on Research and Development (R&D) in other sectors. Graduate salaries for environment-related roles will generally be close to the average.

Overall, it is fair to say that there is no single established pathway to an environmental career in the energy sector, as the range of activities - and the consequent environmental impacts - is so extensive and varied.

Issues and Trends

The major environmental issue facing the energy industry is the need to reduce carbon dioxide emissions from energy sources, in order to prevent major climate change occurring due to the greenhouse gas effect. This reduction will require a major shift from the traditional fossil fuels, which currently dominate the energy supply mix, to 'low carbon' and 'no carbon' energy sources, such as wind energy and solar power. Renewable energy is set to grow rapidly in the next few decades and will provide many new opportunities, although the expansion may not be smooth or uniform across the range of emerging technologies.

There is intense debate and research by governments, academia and industry on how the climate change challenge can be met. At the time of writing, the UN Kyoto Protocol on Climate Change had set out an initial framework for international action and the UK government was in the process of implementing a fundamental review of future energy policy, with the intention of mapping out the UK route to a low carbon economy. There will be increasing worldwide demand for individuals who understand climate change and its implications for countries and companies.

Greatly increased energy efficiency will be an important element of any sustainable energy future. Designing for energy efficiency is an integral part of many professional activities and it will require expert contributions from a wide range of disciplines, including product designers, vehicle designers, architects, planners, civil engineers and building service engineers. There is enormous scope to introduce further energy efficiency measures and individuals who can offer creative solutions for this will be in demand.

In the medium term, a continuing environmental issue for the energy industry is to further reduce emissions and impacts of pollutants that contribute to acidification and health impacts, such as sulphur dioxide and particulates. Energy companies will need individuals who understand how they can respond effectively and efficiently to meet European Union Directives and national legislation to minimise pollution.

Whatever the future, extraction of fossil fuels will continue to be required through this century. As the more inaccessible and environmentally sensitive sources are extracted, there will be an increasing need for novel solutions to minimise the potential environmental effects.

Personal Profiles

David Acres - Environmental Projects Manager, TXU Energy

"I graduated in Engineering from Cambridge University in 1987. Initially I worked on the design of civil engineering projects, becoming a Chartered Civil Engineer and CIWEM member.

My work increasingly included the environmental management of construction impacts, which I found an interesting challenge. I decided to shift my career pathway into environment and completed a Masters degree in Environmental Management at Strathclyde University in 1996. Following this I worked for Scottish Power on environmental impact assessments of new power stations, including air dispersion modelling studies. I then joined WS Atkins Environment and worked as an environmental consultant, with an increasing involvement in air quality management of industrial sources, such as power stations.

My most recent move took me to TXU Energy as an Environmental Projects Manager. I manage projects to manage the environmental impacts of electricity generation, working with the Environment Agency and local authorities to develop cost-effective solutions. Issues arising span the full range of environmental concerns, such as ecology, air quality, water quality, contaminated land and pollution abatement techniques. I also co-ordinate the implementation of environmental management systems across the organisation. A main appeal of the role is the very wide range of tasks - the corresponding challenge is to maintain an understanding of all the issues, while drawing on specialist advice when necessary."

Ian Housley - CTC Environmental

"I run my own consultancy, CTC Environmental, which I established in 1999. CTC Environmental specialises in environmental regulation such as Integrated Pollution Control (IPC), Integrated Pollution Prevention and Control (IPPC) and environmental management systems. CTC Environmental's clients include the Department for Environment, Food and Rural Affairs (DEFRA), the Environment Agency, Lloyds Register International Power Group, TXU Europe and BHP Billiton.

Prior to establishing CTC Environmental, I worked for National Power for 25 years in a variety of posts. My career started in Control and Instrumentation, being responsible for power station control systems. From 1990 I was responsible for environmental management systems and their development, environmental compliance, environmental standards, audit advice, policy implementation and public environmental performance reporting, both for the UK plant and international portfolio.

I have a Royal Society of Health Diploma in Environmental Protection, a postgraduate diploma in Environmental Quality Management, and an MSc in Environmental Quality Management. I am a Director of the Institute of Environmental Management, of which I am a member, and am registered as a Principal Environmental Auditor with the UK's Environmental Auditors Registration Association (EARA)."

Contacts

Association for the Conservation of Energy (ACE)
Westgate House, Probend Street, London N1 8PT
www.ukace.org

British Nuclear Energy Society
1-7 Great George Street, London SW1P 3AA
www.bnes.com

British Wind Energy Association
26 Spring Street, London W2 1JA
www.bwea.com

Centre for Alternative Technologies
Machynlleth, Powys SY20 9AZ
www.cat.org.uk

Climate Action Network (CAN)
31 Pitfield Street, London N1 6HB
www.climatenetwork.org.uk

Combined Heat and Power Association
Grosvenor Gardens House, 35-37 Grosvenor Gardens, London SW1W 0BS
www.chpa.co.uk

Electricity Association
30 Millbank, London SW1P 4RD
www.electricity.org.uk

Electric Vehicle Association
17 Westmeston Avenue, Rottingdean, East Sussex BN2 8AL
www.gwasoc.dircon.co.uk/evahome.html

Energy from Waste Association
26 Spring Street, London W2 1JA
www.efw.org.uk

The Energy Saving Trust
21 Dartmouth Street, London SW1H 9BP
www.est.org.uk

Environmental Transport Association
10 Church Street, Weybridge, Surrey KT13 8RS
www.eta.co.uk

IEA Coal Research Ltd
Gemini House, 10-18 Putney Hill, London SW15
www.iea-coal.org.uk

Institute of Energy
18 Devonshire Street, London W1G 2AU
www.instenergy.org.uk

Institute of Petroleum
61 New Cavendish Street, London W1M 8AR
www.petroleum.co.uk

National Energy Foundation
National Energy Centre, Dary Avenue, Knowle Hill, Milton Keynes MK5 8NG
www.natenergy.org.uk

Society of British Gas Industries
36 Holly Walk, Leamington Spa, Warks CV32 4LY
www.sbgi.org.uk

UK Petroleum Industry Association
9 Kingsway, London WC2B 6XF
www.ukpia.com

Magazines

UK Power magazine
www.ukpoweronline.co.uk

World Oil magazine
www.worldoil.com

25. Transport & Logistics

Chris Fry, Transport Research Laboratory

The Sector

The transport and logistics sector encompasses the planning and provision of infrastructure and services to enable the movement of people and goods. It encompasses a number of 'modes' (i.e. rail, light rail, road, walking, cycling, air, inland waterways and shipping) and importantly, the links between them.

Transport is an essential requirement for everyone and is currently in need of revitalisation in the UK. Some of the main issues for the sector, outlined in the Government's '10 Year Plan', relate to improving accessibility for all through an expanded public transport network, reducing congestion on the roads and improving safety.

It is widely recognised that transport gives rise to major environmental impacts, from the loss of wildlife associated with new infrastructure to the contribution to global warming and local air pollution problems associated with the emissions from operating vehicles. Proper consideration of environmental concerns is therefore crucial to the sector.

Sector Profile

The transport and logistics sector is large and diverse. Major private sector employers include transport operators, distribution companies and consultants whilst public sector employers include local and national government. The rail industry alone, now primarily privately owned, is estimated to employ approximately 150,000 people.

The sector is growing in response to the current investment in the sector. In particular, there is a shortage of trained transport planners working for local authorities and consultants who are needed to undertake strategic studies and develop scheme proposals. The number of transport planners was estimated to be around 3,500 in 2002, a number which is expected to need to increase by 50% by 2004.

No specific information is available on how many environmental professionals work wholly or largely in the transport and logistics sector. However, with many environmental jobs linked to transport planning, appraisal and implementation, the upward trend in jobs in the sector generally is likely to be mirrored amongst environmental professionals working in transport.

Typical Post Names

Transport Planner, Transport Engineer, Transport Advisor, Fleet Manager, Logistics/ Distribution Manager, Transport Consultant, Transport Officer, Technician

Main Employers

- Department for Transport
- Highways Agency
- Railtrack

- Local authorities
- Train operating companies e.g. South West Trains, Virgin Trains
- Air industry e.g. British Airports Authority
- Vehicle (and component) manufacturers
- Consultancies e.g. Arup, Halcrow, Jacobs, MVA, Scott Wilson, WS Atkins, WSP

Career Opportunities

Environmental professionals working in consultancy positions will commonly have some involvement in the transport and logistics sector. For example, transport experience may be gained through undertaking Environmental Impact Assessments for road or rail infrastructure proposals or appraising Multi-Modal Studies. Another overlap might be through the development of an Environmental Management System for a company or public authority with a large transport or logistics remit.

Environmental consultants are likely to have a primary qualification in environmental science/planning or in a specialist environmental discipline (e.g. ecology, noise/vibration or landscape architecture). Consultants wishing to specialise in this field may benefit from a further academic or professional qualification in some aspect of transport.

Public sector and non-profit making environmental bodies also have need for environmental professionals with a good understanding of the transport sector in order respond to case work on transport projects and related development proposals. Of the statutory environmental bodies, the Countryside Agency is unique in also having a specific transport-related responsibility for rural communities.

A specialist career in transport planning (e.g. working for a consultancy or local authority) is best launched following the achievement of a transport planning qualification, currently most commonly taught by universities at Masters degree level. Similarly, engineering positions in the sector traditionally require a civil engineering degree, perhaps combined with a transport-specific postgraduate qualification.

Of particular relevance to the development of future career opportunities in the transport planning arena is the Transport Planning Skills Initiative (coordinated by the Transport Planning Society). This was launched in April 2002 and is providing a focus for a programme of action to increase the number of transport planners to meet expected demands. The Initiative is targeted at the training needs of those already in the profession, increasing awareness amongst sixth formers and undergraduates and facilitating professionals from other backgrounds to move into the transport field.

In the private sector, there are many opportunities relating to logistics planning and implementation. Many such jobs are with major manufacturing or retail companies, specialist logistics service providers and consultancy companies.

Issues and Trends

According to Government figures, in 1998/2000 the average British resident travelled nearly 7000 miles per year, an increase of 6% since 1989/91. Car travel accounts for approximately four fifths of the total passenger miles travelled and nearly all freight miles.

However, the provision and use of transport infrastructure has an environmental cost associated with it. The rising demand for transport is coinciding with the introduction of legislative requirements and high public expectations relating to environmental protection. Transport policy development requires a careful balancing act between economic (e.g. regeneration), social (e.g. equitable access to services) and environmental (e.g. noise, air pollution, biodiversity, landscape impacts) concerns when considering transport issues. Progress has been made in improving the way that regional and local decisions are reached through the introduction of the 'New Approach to Appraisal' which provides a framework for weighing up the potentially conflicting issues. In addition new types of plans and studies such as Multi-Modal Studies are now being undertaken to ensure that in solving particular bottlenecks, options for all transport modes (road, rail, cycling etc) are considered.

Globally, the increasing prosperity in some developing nations and the lifting of international trade barriers and advances in technology are driving the increased movement of people and goods across international boundaries. For many populations, increasing personal mobility is having a positive effect on the local economy and improving access to basic services, but may in turn put extra pressure on the environment. For the movement of goods, supply chain and logistical issues are exercising many international companies as they strive to reach new markets.

Overseas opportunities in the transport sector associated with the provision or maintenance of infrastructure are commonly available to people working in UK engineering and environmental consultancy companies. Similarly, overseas opportunities are available in the logistics field (e.g. through working for a multinational manufacturing company).

Personal Profiles

Dominic McGrath - Transport Strategy Team Leader, Basingstoke & Deane Borough Council

"Having decided to make a career change after seven years working in banking, I studied for a BSc (Hons) in Environmental Planning at Anglia Polytechnic in Chelmsford, Essex. This was a Royal Town Planning Association accredited course, from which I graduated in 1990.

My first transport planning job was with Leicestershire County Council, as a Planning Assistant. I worked within the Structure Plan team focusing on transport and economy policy development. The Structure Plan is the strategic element of the 'Development Plan' which sets out policies guiding the location of development and associated infrastructure. Much of my work focussed on developing the Council's 'Transport Choice' policy which sought to guide major development to the most sustainable locations, based around locations within identified corridors well served by high quality bus and rail services.

After two years in that post I moved to Berkshire County Council. At that time consultants, under contract to the Council, provided all planning and transport services for the Council. My role was Contract Manager within the County Council's client unit. This provided a much wider range of experience than might otherwise have been available at that level. Projects included the development of cycle networks, the securing of local bus services and the setting up of a bicycle recycling scheme under the Government's cycle challenge.

Four years ago I moved on to work for Basingstoke and Deane Borough Council. Moving from a County to a District level authority represents a major shift within the local authority sector and this is reflected in the scope of work. There is much greater emphasis on implementation of local transport schemes. There is also a much greater advisory role to colleagues elsewhere within the Council. My current responsibilities include developing a Park & Ride scheme, introducing 'Safer Journeys to School' initiatives and liaison with local businesses on Green Travel Plans. Basingstoke & Deane has recently been selected as a case study for a national best practice study on Travel Plans."

Sujith Kollamthodi - Senior Environmental Research Scientist, TRL Limited

"After completing a BSc in Chemistry and an MSc in Automotive Engineering, I began my working career in the motor industry working for what was then Rover Group as a body structural engineer, specialising in noise and vibration issues. The three years that I spent at Rover gave me a very solid grounding in engineering design, research and development, and allowed me to develop key skills such as preparing and presenting training courses.

When the time came to move on, the noise and vibration skills that I had gained at Rover left me well placed to change my career path and move into the environment sector, whilst still allowing me to retain a focus on transport and the motor industry. TRL initially recruited me as an environmental noise specialist focussing on traffic noise, with a particular emphasis on tyre/road noise. This work involved a range of test and analysis work to investigate the generating mechanisms responsible for tyre/road noise, as well as studies to develop new test techniques for measuring environmental noise pollution.

I have always been very keen to broaden the range of my skills, and consequently it was very important for me to work for a company with interests in a number of environmental fields, which actively encouraged its staff to develop their career interests. Working for TRL has allowed me to branch out into the areas of transport-generated air pollution, and sustainability, and to develop my project management skills. Amongst other projects, in the last year I have investigated the levels of regulated emissions from different types of road transport, assessed the acoustic performance of road surface treatments, and conducted a study to examine the implications of implementing the End-of-Life Vehicle Directive in the UK. After two and a half years at TRL, I now manage a wide-ranging portfolio of research and consultancy work, covering transport-generated air and noise pollution, and motor industry sustainability issues."

Contacts

Department for Transport
www.dft.gov.uk

Highways Agency
www.highways.gov.uk

Institute of Civil Engineers (ICE)
www.ice.org.uk

Institution of Highways and Transportation (IHT)
www.iht.org

Institute of Logistics and Transport (IOLT)
www.iolt.org.uk/careers

Railtrack
www.railtrack.co.uk

Royal Town Planning Institute (RTPI)
www.rtpi.org.uk

Society of Motor Manufacturers and Traders (SMMT)
www.smmt.co.uk

Strategic Rail Authority
www.sra.gov.uk

Transport for London
www.tfl.gov.uk

Transport Planning Society
www.tps.org.uk

TRL Limited
www.trl.co.uk

Portal sites/e-mail news services

New Civil Engineer Web Services
www.nceplus.co.uk

Rail Industry Training Council
www.ritc.org.uk

The Transport Web
www.transportweb.com

Recruitment Agencies

Beresford Blake Thomas
www.bbt.co.uk

Hays Montrose
www.haysworks.com

Locate
www.locatepartnership.co.uk

Peter James and Partners
www.pjp.uk.com

Magazines

Local Transport Today - provides fortnightly news, analysis, comment and information on jobs in the UK transport scene
www.landor.co.uk/ltt/Index.htm

26. Environmental Policy

Justin Taberham, CIWEM

The Sector

The issue of environmental policy involves and impacts a large number of people employed in the environment sector. Policy dictates and governs much of the activity that takes place in the sector, from strategic plans at Government level to fieldwork. Many employees are involved with environmental policy issues for part of their jobs, however, there are relatively few people who work in environmental policy full time.

Policy-making is concerned with the formulation of strategies and plans for action, for example the development of an action plan for the implementation of a European Directive in the UK, or setting out how a local authority can deliver a sustainable waste management obligation. Policy is very closely tied to legislation. It both influences, and is in turn influenced by legislation (policies can be enshrined in law, if necessary, and new legislation will often require the development of corresponding new policy). The focus is on objectives and actions - defining objectives and working out how these can be delivered effectively within existing institutional frameworks. As with environmental law, the main driver for environmental policy in the UK is the European Commission (EC) through its Directives, and consequently an awareness of current and future EU policy and legislation is highly advantageous.

The process of delivering environmental policies is such that there is now great scope for the involvement of 'stakeholders', or interested parties. These could be industry representatives, local authorities or non-governmental organisations (NGOs) from the not-for-profit sector who represent a given interest group. Such opportunity for involvement has grown in recent years with the importance that has been attached to 'transparency' in government.

As a result of the increase in potential for involvement in the decision-making and policy formulation process, and the increasing emergence of the environment as a global issue, the environmental policy sector is very diverse. Policies can be developed at a very small, local level, or on a global scale e.g. the Kyoto Protocol to the United Nations Framework Convention on Climate Change. Hence, there is the opportunity for involvement in a variety of issues and at many different levels.

Sector Profile

The sector employs around 1000 people full time in the UK, mainly in central government (Department for Environment, Food & Rural Affairs, Department for Transport, Office of the Deputy Prime Minister), government agencies and regulators (Environment Agency, Scottish Environment Protection Agency, Office of Water Services), NGOs and consultancies. There are many more people who have environmental policy as part of their day to day work, but the number of people working purely in environmental policy is low. The number employed in the sector is steadily growing as organisations seek to get actively involved in the process of policy making for an increasing level of new legislation, often from EC Directives. Many companies and organisations hire environmental policy specialists to 'light lobby' i.e. try to influence policy by reasonable means such as consultation, technical report writing and liaison/meetings with policy makers. Lobbyists have been excluded from this sector profile, as they work within many fields, not just environmental policy.

Typical Post Names

Policy Officer, Policy Advisor, Scientific Officer (Policy), Director of Policy, Director of Public Affairs.

Main Employers

Government Departments (DEFRA and others), larger NGOs, Environment Agency, SEPA, Local Government, larger environment sector utilities and consultancies.

Career Opportunities

Most new entrants into the sector are graduates in an environmental or natural sciences subject. Any experience you might have gained through work placements or previous employment will be of great help. This need not necessarily be direct policy experience, but a position which required the ability to quickly research, read and digest technical material, together with good report writing skills and some exposure to legislation and management plans should ensure that you have the core skills required.

Many people also hold second degrees such as MScs in a relevant area, which is of benefit if policy jobs are sought where specific experience of a policy area (perhaps water, waste or nature conservation) is needed. A large proportion of those working in environmental policy have followed a circuitous route to their current posts, often having experience of several areas of environment sector work with varied employers.

Starting salaries for new graduates in a Policy Officer position vary from £12,000 to £20,000. As with many other positions in the 'not-for-profit' sector, salaries vary widely with some organisations offering low salaries and relying on staff enthusiasm and commitment to make up for this. Policy positions which require experience in a specific field often attract higher salaries. Local and central government policy positions can be relatively well paid, with some starting salaries higher than £20,000.

Senior Policy positions attract much higher salaries, but higher level positions are often filled by people with long track records in specific sectors. Employees in the policy sector are often multi-skilled 'generalists', but they also require in-depth knowledge of many subject areas as well. Team leader positions, co-ordinating policy teams and central strategy, can be relatively well paid. Recently advertised positions have varied from £35,000 up to £80,000. Central policy positions in large private companies may attract even higher salaries.

Senior policy positions can be a good route to senior management, as policy people normally have experience and involvement in key strategic issues affecting all aspects of a company or organisation's business performance. In addition, communication and diplomacy skills are often a requirement of the post.

Issues and Trends

There are an increasing number of environmental policy positions available. This is due to the increasing number of EC Directives (e.g. the Habitats Directive, Landfill

Directive and Water Framework Directive) and other varied policy publications, which require detailed analysis, production and consultation. Allied with this is an increased understanding that specific staff with policy experience are needed, rather than making do with policy being a part of other positions. Producing effective policy is becoming a more public exercise, and this has knock-on benefits to employment in this sector.

The move to a more global market in trade, let alone enlargement of the EC, and the globalisation of the world environment sector has increased future opportunity for environmental policy specialists in the UK to work overseas. Global environment sector policy experts and teams will become commonplace in the next decade.

Personal Profiles

Kirsty Lewin - Head of Water Policy, RSPB

"Getting the first policy job is always the hardest. After that, there are many openings. When I left school I trained as a nurse. After some years travelling I wanted a change, went back to university and took a degree in political science. I got my first policy job immediately after graduation with the Ministry for the Environment in New Zealand. I started as a researcher in its 'think thank' - the Strategic Policy Group. There I worked on a range of environmental issues for the government - from setting priorities between different environmental problems, to issues around environmental ethics and environmental justice. While at the Ministry, I was promoted several times, and spent my final year working on sustainable land management issues in the Land Team as a policy analyst. While at the Ministry I completed a Masters degree in Environmental Science, and wrote my thesis on the ethics of genetically engineering farm animals.

After five years in an office environment, I wanted to get my hands dirty and spend some time in a real farm environment. I went to Ladakh, in the Indian Himalayas, and spent three months working as a volunteer on a small family subsistence farm - learning the basics of organic farming at high altitude (it was around 3500 metres). All the work there was manual, and Buddhism and Ladakhi culture was prominent in the planning and work of the farm. I left Ladakh with a great awareness of the impacts of globalisation on small agricultural communities, and how policy decisions in one country can greatly affect small communities many thousands of miles away.

On arriving in the UK, I took a job with the RSPB's Water Policy team. I am now head of the team, and we work on all national (and some European) water issues which affect the wetland habitat and species priorities of the RSPB. For example, we work on flood defence, water quality, water quantity, pollution, biodiversity issues and land and water management planning. My work is fascinating - and different each day.

Policy work requires a broad range of skills - many of which are learned 'on the job'. It is important to work with the media to maintain a high profile. RSPB policy employees analyse scientific papers, develop new policies in response to current government ones, respond to government consultations, keep up to speed with new thinking, speak at seminars and conferences, organise and lead workshops, lobby MPs and government officials, work with local communities, encourage the participation of our RSPB members, write articles for journals and magazines, talk to members of the public and community groups, and communicate our messages both within and outside the organisation. It is most important to be passionate, enthusiastic and willing to learn."

Justin Taberham - Director of Policy, CIWEM

"My current position at CIWEM is quite complex and varied. I oversee a team of Policy Officers and as a team we discuss key policy themes for the future and liaise and consult with Government and Regulators over current and forthcoming policy. At the same time, we manage a network of technical panels and contacts who give us technical backup so that we are able to respond to issues beyond our personal areas of experience. We also propose and produce conferences, policy statements and publications so we can take issues forward with sound science rather than depend upon the same old arguments (some say that you could write the comments of some organisations based on their responses 50 years ago).

We liaise regularly with a large number of organisations, and personal relationship-building and networking is key to my position. Information sharing is a good way to avoid duplication and it often helps to have the whole story rather than hear snippets. Trust develops between policy makers and policy 'changers' over a period of time and this trust is essential to policy work. There is no place for gossip when you are regularly asked to back up what you have said and why you have said it. Keeping up to date with current issues is very important, and we have a large list of journals and magazines we regularly read. We also heavily use the internet to keep up to date with environmental issues worldwide.

My career history is varied but all points to what I am currently doing. When I was a kid, my father introduced me to fishing, walking and enjoying the countryside. His father had done the same for him. From an early age I was really keen to do something for the environment (probably the same sentiment as a lot of the younger readers of this book). In the early 1980s I was very involved in rainforest issues, endangered species and practical conservation work (various conservation holidays and membership of green groups - I even bought a patch of rainforest to stop it being sold to an oil company!). I drifted through education and just did the A Levels that I would get the best results in. I then made a key decision to take an environmental degree, but one where I would come out with a year's employment too - a sandwich degree (Please see Chapter 4 on 'Student Placements' as it explains the value of this approach). I did an Environmental Studies degree at what was then Hatfield Polytechnic (now University of Hertfordshire) because I knew they had a placement in fisheries with Thames Water. With the confidence that I'd get the placement, I did the degree, and did get the placement that I was after.

I finished the degree, which I absolutely loved, and within three months had landed a fisheries position with what was National Rivers Authority (NRA - now Environment Agency). I spent six years with NRA/EA, working up to the level of Fisheries and Recreation Officer. My job over those years changed from being largely field-based to one where strategy, policy, budgets, projects and plans were predominant. I then moved to London to work as Operations Manager for the Inland Waterways Association (IWA), a waterways charity. The work there involved a large amount of consultation with Government and Regulators and public relations issues as well as financial management. After two years at IWA, I moved to my current position at CIWEM. My career has naturally developed in the direction of environmental policy and I thoroughly enjoy seeing new policy developed and negotiated. It's nice to think that you are in there at the start of policy with a chance to change things for the better. I still want to make the world better, but I think I'm in a better position now than I ever was to do this."

Robin Carter - Policy Adviser and Executive Officer, Department for Environment, Food & Rural Affairs (DEFRA)

"I graduated in Business from the University of Hertfordshire in 1992, thereafter I travelled and worked informally in South East Asia and Australia for two and a half years. During this time I was fortunate to be involved in research into the coping strategies of rural tribes in Sarawak, particularly with regard to traditional medicine use.

Returning to England in 1997 I soon headed back to Asia - to Japan, where I taught English for a private education chain called GEOS. While I knew that I was not 'vocationally' motivated to undertake further education in teaching methodology, I learnt much about how to instruct and impart information simply and accurately. This has stood me in good stead ever since.

I returned to London in 2000 and undertook an Open University primer course in Third World Development before joining the School of Oriental and African Studies' MA in Environment and Development. During the MA I focused on rural development techniques (which are similar to basic teaching techniques) and computerised map-making (GIS) followed by a thesis on the use of traditional medicine at village level in Laos.

While I had intended to work overseas in rural development, I found myself under-qualified to compete for the very few positions available related to traditional medicine. I turned my attention to the civil service, aware that there were many internal openings and opportunities for training. While I had previously thought of the civil service as 'old school' I was pleasantly surprised to find that my 'real world' experiences were as valuable as my academic history.

I am now a Policy Adviser working in the Environment, Business and Consumers section of the Department of Environment, Food and Rural Affairs. I am currently dealing with how best to create a government policy for taking forward an idea called resource productivity (how to make more products from less resources while at the same time making less waste and polluting less). My work involves a lot of literary research into past and present UK environmental policy, keeping up to date on developments through contact with colleagues in waste, energy, air quality and water as well as writing first drafts of speeches for the Environment Minister.

After I have completed my one year probation period I will be able to move to another area of the civil service much more easily than if I was applying from outside the organisation. I will have to consider if I want to move to the Department for International Development where I might be able to progress with my original thoughts of rural development, or maybe the Environment Agency where I could use my map-making skills. Wherever I go it will be my choice to stay within environmental work.

My message would be that whatever your background, you can work within the environmental sector. Employers today are much more interested in your life experience and people skills than they are in a long list of qualifications in a specific field. The people I work with do so because they are interested in the area, not necessarily because they are formally qualified to do so."

Duncan Huggett - Senior Policy Officer, RSPB

"As a Senior Policy Officer at the RSPB, I am responsible for all matters relating to the effective implementation of policy and law relating to the protection of important wildlife sites. This involves the analysis of existing national and international policy and law. At an international level, this includes the Ramsar Convention and Oslo-Paris Convention (OSPAR), inputting into Ministerial and annual meetings, and participating in specialist working groups such as the development of threatened and declining habitats and species selection criteria. At a European level, the focus of work is the EU 'Birds' and 'Habitats' Directives, working with other European BirdLife partners to identify and protect Special Protection Areas and Special Areas of Conservation.

At a national level, the Wildlife and Countryside Act is the main instrument for site protection. After a detailed analysis of the failings of the legislation and associated policies, NGOs were successful in persuading Government to introduce legislation to strengthen wildlife site protection. The Countryside & Rights of Way Act was the culmination of several years work, responding to Government consultation papers, negotiating with civil servants, developing legislative proposals, promoting amendments and lobby MPs in both the Houses of Commons and Lords. More recently, legislation to protect nationally important marine sites was promoted as a private members bill, although this has yet to be completed.

I actually have no formal training in law or political lobbying. I have two degrees in biology and my background is scientific. I started working for the RSPB over 10 years ago on a series of short-term contracts. However, a scientific and analytical approach to problem solving has proved the most valuable experience for working in nature conservation policy and law. Over the years, work has involved grappling with a wide range of issues including fisheries, flood and coastal defence, coastal zone management and transport. It has involved working in many diverse places, from local nature reserves to the House of Commons and many places abroad."

Contacts

Centre for Social and Economic Research on the Global Environment
www.uea.ac.uk/env/cserge

The Chartered Institution of Water and Environmental Management
www.ciwem.com

Department for the Environment, Food and Rural Affairs
www.defra.gov.uk

Department for the Environment in Northern Ireland
www.doeni.gov.uk

Department for Transport
www.dft.gov.uk

English Nature
www.englishnature.org.uk

Environment Agency
www.environment-agency.gov.uk

Environment Council
www.environment-council.org.uk

Environmental Data Interactive Exchange website
www.edie.net

Environmental Data Services (ENDS) Report
www.ends.co.uk

Environment Post
www.environmentpost.co.uk

Environment, Transport and Regional Affairs Committee
www.parliament.uk/commons/selcom/etrahome

European Environment Agency
www.eea.eu.int

European Union On-line
www.europa.eu.int

Friends of the Earth
www.foe.co.uk

Greenpeace
www.greenpeace.org.uk

The Guardian Newspaper
www.guardian.co.uk

Institute for European Environmental Policy
www.ieep.org.uk

Journal of Environmental Policy & Planning
www.cf.ac.uk/cplan/jepp/jepphome.html

New Scientist
www.newscientist.com

Office of the Deputy Prime Minister
www.odpm.gov.uk

Royal Society for the Protection of Birds
www.rspb.org.uk

Scottish Environment Protection Agency
www.sepa.org.uk

United Nations Environment Programme
www.unep.org

US Environmental Protection Agency
www.epa.gov

World Wildlife Fund
www.wwf.org.uk

27. Environmental Law

Mark Brumwell & Sue Davidson, SJ Berwin

We are grateful for the assistance given by Rachel Devine from Schlumberger, and Tony Plytas and Anne Harrison from the Environment Agency.

The Sector

The Environmental Law sector encompasses legal careers in a variety of forms. These include providing legal advice to private law firm clients, prosecuting offenders for breaches of environmental law for the Environment Agency, advising on environmental law and policy initiatives within local and central government, and providing in-house legal advice on environmental issues to corporations.

The main lead in the development of environmental law in the UK comes from the European Union (EU) through Directives, and the UK is under constant pressure to implement and enforce the increasing number of environmental Directives issued by the EU. As a result, the UK environmental law regime is subject to constant development and people working within the environmental law area need to be familiar not only with the current regime, but also with any proposals for changes to that regime. Key issues within the environmental law sector are the formulation of environmental law in Europe and the UK, compliance with environmental law, potential environmental liability under statute and common law, and the rights of individuals and groups under environmental law.

Typical Post Names

Solicitor, Senior Solicitor, Assistant Solicitor

Main Employers

Private law firms, Environment Agency, central and local Government, non-governmental organisations (NGOs), European Institutions, industry.

Career Opportunities

Private sector
In order to qualify as a solicitor in England, a candidate must complete an appropriate law qualification and complete a two-year traineeship at an appropriate organisation. If the traineeship is with a private law firm, it may be possible to spend part of that traineeship within the firm's environment department (if there is one). Currently, a first year trainee in a top rank private law firm in London could expect to receive a salary of about £25,000 per annum increasing to about £30,000 as a second year trainee and about £50,000 as a newly qualified solicitor. Salaries outside London and in smaller firms within London are likely to be substantially lower. A specialisation in an area of environmental study is also useful, for example environmental law, environmental science or environmental economics.

Public Sector
The Environment Agency employs teams of advisory and prosecution lawyers in each of its eight Regions and at its Head Office in Bristol. Positions are available not only for fully qualified barristers and solicitors but also for legal executives and

'non-qualified' legal assistants. A law degree is essential and a science background is also useful. Lawyers within the Environment Agency may advise or prosecute on any of the environmental law regimes within the Agency's remit, from waste regulation and pollution prevention and control to flood defence, water resources and navigation law. They also require a thorough understanding of general public law and over-arching issues such as human rights. Traineeships are sometimes available. Salaries for newly qualified solicitors or barristers start in the region of £20,000 to £28,000 and can rise to about £40,000 for a principal solicitor or counsel of several years' experience. Each of the Regions has a Regional Solicitor or Counsel who is responsible for the legal services provided in that region. All Environment Agency job vacancies are advertised on its website at www.environment-agency.gov.uk.

Industry
An environmental lawyer working in-house for industry needs to be a qualified lawyer and have several years' experience as an environmental lawyer within a private law firm. Salaries depend upon experience brought to the position and the scope of work required. Generally in-house lawyers expect slightly less salary than top ranking firms in the private sector, however, they tend to receive greater indirect benefits than a lawyer in private practice, such as shares, extensive health insurance and travel. In general, organisations that employ environmental lawyers are organisations whose activities have potentially significant impact on the environment and are aware that poor environmental performance creates adverse publicity, and impacts on the financial bottom line by increasing costs and diverting management time. Industry employers also tend to be organisations large enough to support not only generalist in-house lawyers but also specialist environmental lawyers. As a result there are fewer positions for environmental lawyers in-house than in private practice. There is a wide selection of industry sectors where an environmental lawyer may work. These include transport, water, waste, communications, and power supply, as well as oil and gas exploration and production.

Issues and Trends

Water Management
The Water Framework Directive has placed a new focus on the management of Europe's water resources. The Directive will have implications for each Member State's legal regime for the regulation of water quality and quantity. The Directive poses new challenges to Government, the water industry, and the agricultural sector and will impact on every individual who consumes water or directly or indirectly pollutes water.

Waste Management
The Landfill Directive 1999 requires Member States to address the increasing quantities of biodegradable waste that is being disposed of by landfill, by setting targets for reducing or eliminating the disposal of certain wastes by landfill. The Directive also encourages waste prevention, recycling and recovery, and the use of recovered materials and energy so that natural resources are used more efficiently. The targets in the Directive will pose a significant challenge for Member States. In the UK in particular, local authorities must now change their approach to waste management. It is expected that there will be considerable activity in this area as local authorities seek to encourage waste minimisation, re-use and recycling, and secure alternative methods of waste disposal.

Climate Change
The EU has agreed to ratify the Kyoto Protocol on greenhouse gases, which sets strict greenhouse gas emission reduction targets. In anticipation, the UK has introduced a climate change levy, which took effect on 1 April 2001. Also, the UK has launched the world's first greenhouse gas emissions trading regime, where rights to emit greenhouse gases are allocated and then may be traded between participants. Law will have a key role in regulating greenhouse gas emissions and thereby contributing to the UK's achievement of its greenhouse gas reduction targets.

Personal Profiles

Mark Brumwell - Partner, Planning and Environment, SJ Berwin

"I am a partner at SJ Berwin specialising in environmental law including land use planning, compulsory purchase and related areas of public law. I advise a wide variety of commercial clients on the environmental aspects of corporate and property transactions including commercial due diligence and issues of contaminated land in redevelopment projects. I also advise environmental regulators, such as the Environment Agency and I have had particular involvement in infrastructure projects, especially flood alleviation schemes, waste water treatment plants and railways. I deal with a wide variety of other environmental issues on a regular basis, including waste management licensing, landfill tax, employee health and safety, environmental impact assessments, environmental audits and nature conservation controls.

I joined SJ Berwin having worked with two other major UK firms and having spent a period on secondment with an Urban Development Corporation, working on urban regeneration projects. I am a Council member of the United Kingdom Environmental Law Association, the former Convenor of UKELA's Water Working Group, a member of the Law Society's Planning Panel, a Legal Associate of the Royal Town Planning Institute and an Associate of the Institution of Environmental Sciences. I regularly write and lecture on a variety of environmentally related topics. I am also the editor of *Cross Border Transactions and Environmental Law*, and a contributor to the *Encyclopaedia of Forms and Precedents*, published by Butterworths."

Rachel Devine - Environment, Health and Safety Counsel, Eastern Hemisphere, Schlumberger Limited

"I work as an in-house environmental lawyer with Schlumberger Limited, and am currently based in Paris, France. I am qualified as a lawyer in New Zealand, England and Wales. I spent six years working in major law firms as an environmental lawyer advising clients about a range of potential environmental liabilities in the context of audits, new projects, acquisitions and divestments, share issues, securitisations, breaches of environmental legislation and potential litigation.

At Schlumberger, I advise on environmental legal issues in Europe, the Commonwealth of Independent States and Africa. My job involves working towards establishing best practice across a blend of countries and cultures and consequently my role involves working with engineers as well as legal and other technical people. Amongst other things, I negotiate with local governments regarding their environmental concerns, addresses compliance issues and advise on environmental liabilities in real estate acquisitions and divestments. I also train people at all levels of the company about legal environmental issues and conduct site audits of properties."

Anne Harrison - Principal Counsel, Environmental Agency

"As Principal Counsel at the Environment Agency, I specialise in large infrastructure project proposals, land use planning, environmental impact assessment, large public inquiries, environmental appeal hearings and land drainage/flood defence and water law issues. I also advise the Environment Agency generally on its statutory powers, duties and responsibilities. I was responsible for the Environment Agency's in-house legal representation at the Public Inquiry into the 5th Terminal at Heathrow and acted as Project Manager and in-house legal support for the Environment Agency's response to the London International Freight Exchange planning, Compulsory Purchase Order and Transport and Works Act applications and Public Inquiries. I have been with the Environment Agency since its formation on 1 April 1996, after a brief period working for the National Rivers Authority (which was superseded by the Environment Agency).

I am a barrister by profession, and my background at the Bar is in general common law, focusing in particular on professional negligence. Since joining the Environment Agency, I have obtained a Masters in environmental law from UCL, London University and am an active member of the UK Environmental Law Association, participating in both the Sustainable Development and Planning Law Working Groups."

Contacts

Chambers and Partners Student Guide to the Legal Profession
www.ChambersandPartners.com

Department for Environment, Food & Rural Affairs
www.defra.gov.uk

Department for Transport
www.dft.gov.uk

Environment Agency
www.environment-agency.gov.uk

Environmental Data Services (ENDS) Report
www.ends.co.uk

The European Commission (Environment)
www.europa.eu.int/comm/environment/index_en.htm

Law Careers
www.lawcareers.net/lcn.asp

Law Society Gazette
www.lawgazette.com

UK Environmental Law Association
www.ukela.org

Recruitment Agencies

Badenoch & Clark
www.badenochandclark.com

Hays ZMB
www.zureka.com

Mcalegal
www.mcaconsulting.co.uk

Michael Page
www.michaelpage.co.uk

Quantica Legal
www.quantica.co.uk

Graduate Recruitment Fairs at Universities

28. Regeneration

Richard Crabtree, Arup

The Sector

Regeneration involves the physical, economic and social rehabilitation of an area. Sometimes individual issues are focused on, but more often issues are combined and integrated. It is a broad sector that relies on the skills of a number of different professions, including those with economic, planning, environmental, community development, landscape, engineering and architectural skills.

Regeneration is usually led by public sector funding through a number of different schemes and funds. These include:
· European Regional Development Fund (ERDF)
· Single Regeneration Budget (SRB) (new funding ceased)
· Objective 1 (European Funding)
· Environmental Action Fund
· Green Spaces and Sustainable Communities Programme
· Neighbourhood Renewal Fund

Although regeneration programmes and initiatives are usually funded by the public sector, they are formulated and implemented by a wide range of public and private sector organisations. Voluntary and community organisations also play a vital role in many regeneration projects and community led regeneration is being increasingly recognised as the most sustainable.

Regeneration projects can focus on a number of issues, including physical improvement of urban or rural environments, economic development, improving access to jobs, enhancing health, improving housing, transport and access, reducing crime, increasing education and skill levels and developing social cohesion and the capacity of the community. Regeneration involves understanding people and how they interact with each other and the environments that they live and work in. Economic, environmental and social sustainability are key considerations in regeneration activities.

Sector Profile

There are tens of thousands of people involved either directly or indirectly in regeneration. There are many different types of roles e.g. strategic development, programme co-ordination, monitoring or 'hands on'.

There has been recent growth in the number of people directly involved in regeneration work, as the Government has been more focussed on regeneration issues. It seems likely that this trend will continue in the short term. It is unlikely that in the long term there will be any reduction in the number of people working in this field.

Typical Post Names

Regeneration Officer, Planner, Community Development Worker, Regeneration Consultant, Environmental Regeneration Coordinator, Planning & Policy Development Officer, Programme Manager, Project Manager, Monitoring Officer, Neighbourhood Safety Co-ordinator

Main Employers

Central Government (e.g. Office of the Deputy Prime Minister), Local Government (e.g. local councils), Government Agencies (e.g. English Partnerships), Urban Regeneration Companies (e.g. Sheffield One), Groundwork Trusts, Regional Development Agencies (e.g. One NorthEast), Consultancies, Local Community Partnerships, Single Regeneration Budget Partnerships, New Deal for Communities organisations.

Career Opportunities

Above all, people working in regeneration should have an interest in people and the environments that they live in. Regeneration involves attempting to increase quality of life though improvements to physical environments, job and training opportunities, social cohesion, health facilities and recreation facilities among others. This can include projects as diverse as developing urban wildlife habitats, community capacity building and meeting people on a day-today basis to gain an understanding of their particular concerns and aspirations.

To work in regeneration it is essential to have vision and be able to think broadly and creatively and consider all the issues involved. It is important to be a good communicator, and to enjoy regular contact with the public and other professions, since cooperation and consultation are usually key aspects of regeneration work. Good organisational and project management skills are also crucial.

Regeneration can be very political, both at the local and national level. An understanding of and interest in political issues is therefore an advantage for certain regeneration jobs, particularly those in regeneration policy or at more senior levels. This should be seen as a challenge, and can make the job intensely interesting and rewarding, if at times a little frustrating! A career in regeneration offers the opportunity to make a real and positive difference to people's lives.

People with a range of qualifications get jobs in regeneration. For many jobs, it is more important to demonstrate an understanding of the many issues involved in regeneration. For specialist positions, qualifications in Town Planning, Landscape Architecture, Economics, Sociology, Architecture or Engineering may be required. For senior positions it is usually necessary to be educated to degree level or above. A number of specialist postgraduate courses are available for those wishing to pursue a career in particular aspects of regeneration such as housing policy, regional economic development, or regeneration and the environment, for example.

Salary will depended on the sector you work in and your level of experience and responsibility. People employed at a senior and executive level in public sector and consultancy positions can expect to earn in excess of £50,000 to £70,000. In the public sector, a graduate salary would typically start at around £14,000 to £16,000, increasing with age and experience. The average public sector regeneration salary is likely to be in the region of £25,000 to £30,000. In the private sector, starting salaries can be higher, typically from £18,000. An experienced regeneration consultant can expect a salary in the region of £35,000 to £40,000. The not-for-profit and voluntary sectors play a significant role in regeneration initiatives, but pay levels are often lower. However, some people consider that these sectors offer some of the most rewarding job opportunities.

The salaries provided above are only indicative, and can vary widely from organisation to organisation, and also depend on your level of responsibility and experience. To get an understanding of the latest opportunities and salaries check the current vacancies for the sectors you might be interested in. These are contained in the trade journals and websites listed at the end of this chapter.

Issues and Trends

Regeneration is a very topical issue. For a number of years, regeneration has been a stated government priority, and a number of new initiatives and organisations have been formed. However, regeneration policy tends to change as different approaches are tried. This relates to the different political philosophies, or recent governments, and also to changes in society and the way we live. In this way, regeneration is a constantly changing occupation, and it is important to consider the need to be adaptable to this change. However, it means that a career in regeneration related work is likely to be varied and interesting.

The current government is taking a more 'hands-on' approach to regeneration, which has increased the importance of community involvement and seen the recent formation of Regional Development Agencies and Urban Regeneration Companies, for example. Local communities and councils also have access to new funds, such as the New Deal for Communities. The government in the 1980s believed that regeneration led by the private sector was more effective, but even during this period substantial amounts of public money were spent on projects such as the London Docklands regeneration. The European Union also takes an active role in regeneration issues, and has funded a number of UK regeneration projects through various programmes.

There are also international regeneration opportunities. This could be through overseas work with a UK based consultancy, through an aid or health organisation or with local agencies. This work could be dealing with more basic issues, such as enabling clean water supplies in developing countries, or dealing with issues similar to those in the UK in places such as Eastern Europe, the USA or Australia.

Personal Profiles

Martin Havenhand - Chief Executive, Yorkshire Forward

"I was appointed as Chief Executive of Yorkshire Forward in November 1998 and took up the post on 1st February 1999. I have many years' experience in the public sector environment. Prior to this appointment I was Chief Executive of Bassetlaw District Council in North Nottinghamshire for six years. At that time, I was Director and Vice-Chairman of Business Link (North Nottinghamshire) and the Company Secretary of Bassetlaw Development Agency Partnership.

Born in Sheffield, my first job was with Sheffield City Council, and I progressed a career in leisure management and worked for South Yorkshire Metropolitan County Council based in Barnsley for nearly five years up to the mid 1980s. I was involved in the Structure Planning Process and had a leading role in regeneration and economic improvement through planning for and managing the after use of land reclamation sites across South Yorkshire. I then spent eight years at Trafford Metropolitan Borough Council in Greater Manchester as Director of Leisure Services and then Director of Environment working in partnership with Trafford Park Development Corporation and with the Manchester Conurbation Partnerships. I am an active member of a Chief Executive "Action Learning" programme involving colleagues from organizations across Yorkshire and the Humber, and recently completed an MSc Programme in Managing Change through Sheffield Business School and the Centre for Managing Change in London."

Jerome Frost - Associate, Arup

"After completing A-Levels in Physics, Maths and History, I took a year out working at a ski-resort. I then went to The University of Sheffield to study for a BA in Urban Studies and Planning, a three-year course accredited by the Royal Town Planning Institute (RTPI) when followed by the one-year postgraduate Diploma in Town and Regional Planning.

After completing the degree, I chose to specialise and did an MPhil in Land Economy at Cambridge University, before returning to the University of Sheffield to study for the postgraduate Diploma in Town and Regional Planning.

My first job, started whist still studying at Sheffield University, was in development control, dealing with planning applications at the London Borough of Tower Hamlets. After six months in this position, I moved to another local authority job, this time at the London Borough of Brent, where I worked for over two and a half years in development control, but this time working specifically in the Harlesden City Challenge area, which was a major regeneration initiative at the time.

I now work in the Economics and Planning section of Arup, a multi-disciplinary consultancy. I have worked for a range of clients both in the public and private sectors, in locations throughout the country. The range of projects have included research for the government, the redevelopment proposals for the King's Cross area and development of neighbourhood renewal strategies. I am now a Chartered Town Planner and senior regeneration consultant, and I lead on regeneration projects in Arup."

Contacts

There is a great deal of information on the Internet regarding regeneration. The following is a good starting point, and most web sites offer links to more specialised information.

Groundwork
www.groundwork.org.uk
A leading environmental regeneration charity making sustainable development a reality in many of the UK's most disadvantaged communities.

New Start
www.newstartmag.co.uk
A weekly publication for people involved in community regeneration.

Office of the Deputy Prime Minister
www.odpm.gov.uk
This central government department is responsible for delivering the Government's agenda on social exclusion, neighbourhood renewal, planning and regional development. Its website is updated regularly and includes plenty of information about

the different aspects of regeneration.

Regeneration and Renewal
www.regenerationmagazine.com
A weekly publication for people involved in regeneration. This site includes details of current vacancies, an index of consultancies and recent regeneration news and comment. It is good starting point to find out more about the kind of jobs, employers and issues involved in regeneration.

Regen.net
www.regen.net
An information resource for people involved in regeneration. Once registered, it is possible to locate information on the full range of regeneration topics, including rural, urban, community and economic regeneration.

UK Online
www.open.gov.uk
This site provides links to all public sector websites, including regional development agencies, local government sites and urban regeneration companies.

29. Sustainable Development & Local Agenda 21

Tony Adey, Groundwork South Tyneside

The Sector

Local Agenda 21 (LA21) is the process through which communities, businesses and government (the stakeholders) can come together to plan for and implement Sustainable Development. In 1987, a report was produced for the World Commission on Environment and Development, which highlighted that the global rate of natural resource consumption seriously threatened the long-term security of the planet. The Brundtland Report, as it was known, emphasised that significant changes in our everyday activities would be required to avoid future world problems, such as poverty, ill-health and disease, gender imbalance, environmental degradation and accelerating use of natural resources. Consequently, the notion of 'sustainable development' was founded and is described as:

> *"Development which meets the needs of the present without compromising the ability of future generations to meet their own needs."*
> (World Commission on Environment and Development, 1987)

The issues raised by the Brundtland Report led to the 1992 Earth Summit in Rio de Janeiro, which renewed efforts at solving the main threats to our existence. This conference illustrated the need to work towards a 'blueprint' for sustainable development, which became known as 'Agenda 21' (Agenda for the 21st Century). This agenda, or plan, was the most significant of the agreements endorsed by the 150 countries attending the Summit and it vowed to tackle the pressures of the 21st century together as a global community. Although national co-ordination was called for, it was the local level that was targeted as being of greatest significance. It was aimed at ensuring that individual people, communities, businesses, organisations, schools, etc. could identify their exact role in this global plan. Thus, the concept of a 'Local' Agenda 21 was distinguished, with the basic underlying principle of 'think globally, act locally'.

The UK produced a national strategy for sustainable development in 1994, revised in 1999, entitled 'A Better Quality of Life'. This presented four main aims:
- Social progress which recognises the needs of everyone
- Effective protection of the environment
- Prudent use of natural resources
- Maintenance of high and stable levels of growth and employment

Co-ordination of LA21 was to be mainly undertaken by Local Authorities to suit local conditions, and there have been varying levels of commitment. However, a significant amount of work has, and is, being done. Due to the range and diversity of work covered and organisations involved, many people may not realise that their activities do provide an essential contribution to LA21. Above all, LA21 (or, more usually now, 'Sustainability'), is helping people to make the difference.

In 2000, local authorities were given a new duty to ensure the economic, social and environmental well-being of their communities through the development of a 'Community Plan'. These plans have in the main taken over the mantle of LA21 as they are expected to be prepared in a collaborative, top-down/bottom-up manner.

Sector Profile

Most LA21 Officers are employed by local authorities, the most usual departments being Environmental Health, Countryside Services or similar. Some local authorities have set up a whole 'Sustainability' department, with inputs to waste recycling, energy, education, health etc. Increasingly such posts are being located within central policy areas of local authorities and aligned with regeneration activities. Relations with local businesses are also very important; in many districts, especially the metropolitan areas, the regional development agencies act as the link between business and the local authorities.

Of the 50 or so Groundwork Trusts, the majority employ a LA21/Sustainability Officer with the same range of inputs as local authorities, although usually with more emphasis on education, business and organic/community horticulture. In effect, Groundwork Trusts have been 'doing' LA21 since their inception in 1981. Some countryside organisations such as Wildlife Trusts employ LA21 Officers and environmental consultancies are also an option for those with a similar background.

Typical Post Titles

Local Agenda 21 Officer, Sustainability Officer
Some local authorities will have officers in departments such as Environmental Health who will have responsibilities for LA21/Sustainability.

Main Employers

Local authorities, Groundwork Trusts, Wildlife Trusts and similar non-governmental organisations (NGOs), Consultancies

Career Opportunities

As sustainability issues are high on the Government's agenda, career opportunities are reasonable. There are many and varied paths to careers in LA21. Those considered are normally graduates, usually (but not essentially) with a strong environmental bias to their degree, i.e. environmental science or environmental management. A geography degree is quite common, as is biology, botany and geology. Postgraduate specialisation in waste minimisation, energy efficiency, pollution, countryside management, environmental health etc. is desirable, although generalists are probably the norm.

There is no one path to becoming a LA21 Officer; any environmental degree will give you a good grounding for the sector. The ability to tackle the issues raised by global warming, sustainability of resources and other issues relating to sustainable development will require a familiarity with the economic and social implications of the problems and the solutions. Knowledge and experience in these areas will add to the credibility of your presence in the post. Work experience with organisations such as a Groundwork Trust, the British Trust for Conservation Volunteers or a Wildlife Trust is a good prerequisite to a career in Local Government or similar. A job as a warden on a National Trust or RSPB (Royal Society for the Protection of Birds) nature reserve, either paid or as a volunteer, is another useful addition to a CV.

Within a Local Authority, salaries will depend on experience and responsibility, and are based on similar posts. Salary levels will vary in other organisations, but a recent graduate can expect similar rates to those in other environmentally related posts.

Having gained experience in one or more areas of sustainability, there are a wide range of opportunities open to you. Examples include teaching, particularly in further and higher education, environmental work in firms specialising in waste minimisation, energy efficiency, or pollution control, as well as opportunities in a wide variety of environmental improvement firms and organisations, and consultancies.

Issues and Trends

The issues concerned with sustainable development will not go away, and addressing them is becoming ever more urgent. Whilst demonstrable commitment to sustainable development from central Government may appear to fluctuate, the UK is further advanced than many other nations with regard to some aspects of sustainability. By the same token, the UK is not so far advanced as some, particularly in the fields of waste and energy efficiency. There are some very forward thinking local authorities, which have adopted a whole range of waste collection and processing measures, and a major task of LA21 Officers employed by the more reticent councils is to bring them up to speed. Several places in the world, for instance Australia and New Zealand, have adopted a 'zero waste to landfill' policy, to be achieved by 2010. This reduces local taxes and creates important jobs and impetus in the recycling industry.

Education is a vitally important issue, and LA21 personnel have an important role to play in devising and delivering projects for use in schools. Groundwork Trusts have run projects such as Esso Young Energy Savers, WasteSavers, Ollie Recycles, and Greenlink, which have been well received and enjoyed by primary school children. Children pick up a great deal of information regarding sustainability issues and are encouragingly keen and interested. They are often better informed than their teachers, which means that there is an important role for LA21 staff to create and foster links with schools.

Business links are also very important, as there are several recent developments to be addressed, such as landfill tax and issues relating to waste disposal, control of emissions, control of toxic substances etc. Most LA21 Officers will be expected to have enough knowledge to advise local businesses on where to gain advice on the relevant rules and regulations.

Personal Profiles

Frank Price - Principal Consultant, Atkins Environment

"I now have over 20 years experience of environmental work with considerable experience in sustainable development and environmental management. Since joining WS Atkins in February 2000, I have undertaken sustainability reviews and appraisals for a variety of clients and UK District Councils. On behalf of the World Bank I assisted the Government of Delhi in preparing a comprehensive sustainable development action plan for 2021, focussing on the social and environmental aspects of land and natural resource management. I am currently advising the Romanian, Czech and Slovak governments on the implementation of various aspects of sustainable development through developing regimes for public involvement in government decision making. In Romania and the Czech Republic this also involves the implementation of pilot LA21 programmes in a number of district areas.

As a founding member of the Environment Agency's North East Regional Environmental Protection Advisory Committee (REPAC), I have gained wide experience in analysing and advising on issues of regional concern in relation to the Agency's role in environmental protection and sustainable development.

For 10 years prior to joining WS Atkins, I was manager of the Environmental Protection Service in Sheffield City Council, during which time I was responsible for the development and implementation of a city wide approach to sustainable development, environment and health policy and Agenda 21. This involved the integration of economic, social and environmental policies into a cohesive and sustainable strategy for the City's approach to such issues as strategic and site specific land use planning, transport management, the single regeneration budget (SRB) and EC Objective One programmes.

Whilst at Sheffield, I was responsible for implementing an Eco-Management and Audit Scheme (EMAS) throughout the Council and in developing Best Value reviews in respect of environmental performance and environment and health. During this period I also carried out consultancy work for the EU on the development of sustainable development action plans for four European cities. I also worked for one of the emergent democracies of the Russian Federation, for the Danish Environmental Protection Agency on air quality management plans and for the (then) UK Overseas Development Agency advising the Calcutta and West Bengal Governments on sustainable development in relation air quality management."

Cathrine Hall - Head of Environment Strategy, Redcar & Cleveland Borough Council

"After gaining a degree in Zoology in 1973, from Newcastle University, and embarking on a career as a research biologist, laboratory tedium quickly brought on a change of plan. I was fortunate in gaining Local Authority sponsorship to complete another Degree - this time in Environmental Health at Aston University in Birmingham. I thoroughly enjoyed being an Environmental Health Officer, and have worked for several local authorities, steadily moving up the management hierarchy.

In 1997, I became responsible for both Environmental Health and Trading Standards functions within a Unitary Authority. Within this portfolio was the responsibility to develop and implement the Local Agenda 21 strategy for the authority. With one full time member of my staff, who had come to the post as an extremely environmentally committed, qualified teacher, we first started to put the authority's house in order by developing an Environment Strategy.

Reorganisation has recently seen me relinquish responsibility for Environmental Health and Trading Standards, and move to the Chief Executive's Department as Head of Environment Strategy. I work directly with the Chief Executive, and my role is to create the frameworks which help us as a large influential organisation, and through the specific services we provide, and within our community, to lead the way to greater environmental sustainability.

To create this 'environmentally conscious ethos' I have to be a diplomat, an influencer, a networker and a supporter to all those who are moving in the right direction! In other words, I am the main officer 'champion' for the environment within the council. In particular, I have to know how the political and organisational machinery works, to develop with others key strategic documents (e.g. the Municipal Waste Management Strategy, the Affordable Warmth Strategy), and to influence the Community and Strategic Plans.

The Authority is currently considering strengthening the establishment of officers who support me, by the creation of a central unit to co-ordinate environmental management and community engagement."

Tony Adey - LA21 Officer, Groundwork South Tyneside

"I was born in 1940 into a farming background, my father and various other relations working as herdsmen, tractor drivers etc. They, and I, all had an interest in natural history, so a great deal of knowledge regarding flora and fauna was picked up informally as a child. I attended a small village primary school and a not much bigger secondary school, leaving at 15 with no qualifications. However, I worked on a large mixed agricultural estate and was put through all the various departments, culminating in a year at Agricultural College at age 18. Here I gained the National Certificate in Agriculture and read a book that 'changed my life'. It was called Fertility Pastures, by Newman Turner and was my first exposure to organic principles. I have been committed to these principles ever since. Subsequently I worked on a number of organic and other farms and hoped to go into farming on my own account, but never attained the financial wherewithal.

My 'career' has since been extremely varied and includes spells on building sites, at the National Institute for Research in Dairying, 4 years as a partner in a small landscape gardening firm, 2 years as a mason operative (installing natural stone fireplaces), and 7 years in the nuclear industry as a reactor control room assistant.

This brings me up to age 40, and a desire to take a more relevant degree, in order to pursue an interest in archaeology. On completing my degree, I worked in the Archaeology Department of Durham University for 2 years, spending one year writing a book, 'County Durham Through the Ages', and the second year as an Education Officer, 'selling' Archaeology as a school subject. During this period I studied for an Environmental Management Certificate, part time. This was a Community Programme, which only lasted 2 years, but I had a contingency plan to 'do' a Careers Guidance Diploma. Due to the breakup of my marriage, I failed the final exam, but obtained 3 different posts in Employment Training as Training/ Placement Advisor etc. This ended when funding was cut by 50% and I was made redundant, which lasted for a year, during which time I worked voluntarily for the local Wildlife Trust and the Archaeology Department. I then obtained a six-month contract as a Project Officer at Groundwork South Tyneside and have been here ever since - nearly 11 years!

In my time here I have worked a great deal with schools on waste, energy, business links and school grounds improvements and with local business and community groups on a wide range of environmental projects, which have even included archaeology. My spare time interests include being a Tree Warden, local Archaeology groups and being a school governor and part time Countryside Ranger. As you can see, my experience and qualifications inadvertently qualified me for Local Agenda 21 (I was LA21 Officer for two years, during which time I wrote 'Delivering LA21 in South Tyneside') but Groundwork Trusts have been 'doing' it since their inception 21 years ago. Job titles have changed with funding regimes, but the work carried out, although perhaps with different emphases, has remained practically the same."

Contacts

Any Local Councils - Municipal Yearbook
www.knowuk.co.uk/html/about_myb.htm

British Trust for Conservation Volunteers (BTCV)
36 St. Mary's Street, Wallingford, Oxon, OX1 OEU
Tel: 01491 821612
www.btcv.org

www.changingclimate.org
(Website with information on the latest ideas, research and action on all aspects of our changing climate).

Centre for Alternative Technologies
Machynlleth, Powys, SY20 9AZ
www.cat.org.uk

The Club of Rome
Rissener Landstr. 193, 22559 Hamburg, Germany
www.clubofrome.org

The Countryside Agency
John Dower House, Crescent Place, Cheltenham, Gloucestershire, GL50 3RA
www.countryside.gov.uk

Department for Environment, Food and Rural Affairs (DEFRA)
Eland House, Bressenden Place, London SWIE 5DU
Tel: 020 8903000
www.defra.gov.uk
www.doingyourbit.org.uk

Environment Agency
Rio House, Waterside Drive, Aztec West, Almondsbury, Bristol BS32 4UD
www.environment-agency.gov.uk

The Environment Council
212 High Holburn, London, WC1V 7BF
Tel: 020 78362626
www.the-environment-council.org.uk

European Environment Agency
Kongens Nytorv 6, 1050 Copenhagen K, Denmark
Tel: +45 33367100
www.eea.eu.int

The European Union On-line
www.europa.eu.int

Forum for the Future
www.forumforthefuture.org.uk

Global Action Plan
8 Fulwood Place, London, WC1V 6HG
Tel: 020 74055633
Email: all@gapuk.demon.co.uk
www.globalactionplan.org.uk

Global Climate Change Student Guide
www.doc.mmu.ac.uk/aric/gccsg/index

Groundwork UK
85/87 Cornwall Street, Birmingham, B3 3BY
Tel: 0121 236 8565
www.groundwork.org.uk

National Society for Clean Air and Environmental Protection
44 Grand Parade, Brighton, BN2 9QA
Tel: 01273 878 770
www.nsca.org.uk

The Natural Step: www.naturalstep.org

Sustainable Development Commission
www.sd-commission.org

Sustainable Development - the Government's Approach
www.sustainable-development.gov.uk

United Nations Framework Convention on Climate Change
Martin-Luther-King-Strasse 8, D-53175 Bonn, Germany
www.unfccc.int

United Nations Environment Programme
United Nations Avenue, Gigiri, PO Box 30552, Nairobi, Kenya
www.unep.org

United Nations Sustainable Development
www.un.org/esa/sustdev/

References

World Commission on Environment and Development (1987) *Our Common Future.*
Oxford: Oxford University Press, p.43

30. Environment Journalists: An Endangered Species

Alex Kirby, BBC News Online

Being an environment journalist these days is fun, but for many practitioners it's neither glamorous nor secure. Those editors who haven't lost interest in the subject altogether are swayed more now by the contrarians, the people who argue that all's well with this, the best of all possible worlds. Newsroom lore says there are far sexier subjects out there than pollution and the antics of the bunnyhuggers, and the environment correspondents find themselves firmly relegated to the back row of the chorus.

Depending on which part of the mass media you are working in, you will probably be either an environment correspondent or a (more junior) environment reporter. If you work in broadcasting, you may be an environment producer, though few broadcasters have dedicated producers in this area. Whatever your title, you will still need the same range of contacts, whether you confront them with a camera, a microphone or a pen.

Your job will be to tell people about the environmental pressures that are shaping our world. You will need to remember that the cardinal sin for any journalist is to be boring (if you are, nobody except possibly your dog will watch or listen to you, or read your golden prose). So you will have to find ways of covering climate change, genetically modified crops, the latest farming crisis or whatever the story is in an entertaining way. And you'll still have to do it honestly, not writing it up to get a stronger headline out of it, nor pulling your punches for fear of offending proprietors or advertisers.

Usually you will have to settle for simply informing people about the things you think they need to know. You won't often be able to campaign, unless you are an unusual journalist working for an out-of-the-ordinary employer. There's nothing at all wrong with campaigning, and many things right about it. But if direct campaigning is what you really want to do, you may be better off working for someone like Greenpeace or Friends of the Earth. Journalists are usually supposed to try to be objective.

You will probably start off as a news journalist. Many of us stay in news all our working lives, usually from choice. And news has no set agenda. It is concerned with what is happening now, not yesterday, and so the subjects you have to cover can change pretty fast. Few western journalists knew much about the design and performance of Soviet nuclear reactors until the day Chernobyl exploded. As soon as it had, they became instant experts.

Thanks to the internet, most of us can now find information far more quickly than we could only a few years ago. So there's little excuse for saying we don't know enough about a subject to cover it properly. The material is there. What journalists have to do is to know where and how to search for it.

You may in time decide you want to move from news to features, though there's little call for full-time staffers who turn out environment features. You may even decide you want to graduate to punditry and leader-writing, or become a columnist. In any case, you will probably find that the environment is just one subject among several that you cover.

Often that's true in news as well. The environment as an important subject in its own right has declined steadily over the last 10 years (since Margaret Thatcher left office, in fact: she put the environment on the map in a way none of her successors has done). So any journalist who covers the green beat will probably spend time doing stories from overlapping areas as well: science, obviously; farming and rural affairs; energy; trade; animal welfare; development; sometimes even defence.

The national broadsheets, and some of the regional ones, do have dedicated environment writers. Some local papers do as well. The BBC has several at national level, providing radio, TV and online journalism. It also has regional counterparts. But ITN decided some years ago it didn't need anyone, so environment stories are left to its other specialists (often the science correspondent) or to a general news reporter. Sky takes the subject relatively seriously, as does Channel Four, whose science specialist covers it well. There aren't that many environment journalists working in the United Kingdom - enough, with their friends, to fill a fair-sized room in a London pub for the green hacks' Christmas party. There are probably about 20 national environment correspondents working in daily and weekly journalism. And there's not much turnover, at national level at least. We tend to stay in the job for some years.

Whether you work in news or features, the written press, broadcasting or online journalism, you will need to live by your wits. Journalism requires people who are inquisitive, who won't take either "No" or "Yes" for an answer, but who want to get behind the statements to find the facts. The late Nicholas Tomalin of the Sunday Times said journalists needed three things: rat-like cunning, a plausible manner, and a little literary ability. Another British journalist, Hannen Swaffer, once said (and this was many years ago) there was only one question a reporter needed to bear in mind when interviewing a politician: "Why is this lying bastard telling me this particular lie at this particular moment?" Every journalist has to be a thoroughgoing sceptic, but not a cynic.

Living by your wits means having ideas - ideas about what stories to cover, and how to cover them. It means not sitting in front of a computer terminal every day, but spending as much time as you can out of the office, meeting contacts, talking to real people. It means having an ever-expanding and up-to-date contacts book, and keeping your contacts sweet by ringing or messaging them regularly if you can't go to see them. It means being able to recognise a story when you see one, not just when the newsdesk asks you to write one.

If you are confident (or desperate) enough, you may decide not to bother with applying for staff jobs but to work as a freelance. That's often a better option after you've had a few years to establish yourself in your chosen field. You may be a brilliant freelance, but producers and edtors are normally wary of buying in material from people they don't know, which can be a Catch-22 for the beginner.

You will need to like your subject, certainly, but not necessarily to know much about it in detail. There are well-known examples in the trade of experts from one field or another who gravitate to journalism, and then find they don't know how to speak to their audience. Too much knowledge can sometimes get in the way, because one of the key skills in all journalism is knowing what to leave out of a story. You must be able to tell it economically and intelligibly, and that almost invariably means ditching images, soundbites or prose which you've toiled to get and of which you're really proud. It hurts. But it makes a better, crisper story. So a degree in environmental science may help you, and conceivably a media studies qualification might be some use, though that's less certain. Far more important than either, though, are the instincts of a reporter, and the sheer hunger for a story. And that hunger can never be satisfied. Remember, you're only as good as your last story. If you work in the written press, the fate of your morning story is to wrap tonight's fish and chips. If you're a broadcaster, though, your shelf-life is even shorter than that.

It will also help if you can show a prospective employer that you've been around a bit. Someone who has gone straight from school into higher education and who then tries to get a job in journalism is often at a disadvantage. I got quite used to hearing after interviews that I'd failed to get the job because I had a bad career pattern. It was only when I got into mainstream journalism that I realised that was the sort of pattern that most of us had. A university degree, by contrast, was something you didn't mention very much in the newsroom. And I don't think journalism has changed that much since my early days.

If you want to be seriously rich, you probably ought to avoid journalism altogether. There aren't many rich journalists, and that's mainly because it pays very large salaries only to a handful near the top of the pile, though the prodigal appetites of those in the trade have something to do with it as well (there is a reason why Private Eye's legendary red-nosed hack is called Lunchtime O'Booze). Probably the highest-earning environment journalists are making around £70,000 a year, which by the standards of most of us is certainly a lot. But they're the exceptions, and far more will be lucky to earn half that. National journalists are usually fairly well-paid. Regional and local ones sometimes face a real struggle. And most of us start out on local newspapers or radio stations. So be prepared to be skint to start with, anyway.

You may decide to work for the trade or technical press, or for an organisation in the thick of the story, like the Environment Agency or the RSPB, or for some branch of the Government. Alternatively, you may settle on a specialised website, or a magazine which gives a lot of space to the subject. In any case you'll need to find out just what your employer requires of you. And it probably won't be across-the-board coverage, but something much more selective and focussed. It'll be worthwhile, though it won't be the rough-and-tumble of daily news journalism.

You may decide you want to work as a press officer or in public relations (PR) for an organisation involved in the environment. Good press officers who know how the mass media work can help journalists: bad ones are an irrelevance, or worse. A few PR people know how to help, but most are too keen to push their clients' stories to be any real use.

One of the biggest stories most environment journalists have to cover is climate change, or global warming as it's often rather misleadingly called (it's misleading because often the consequence will be regional cooling). Biodiversity loss, the extinction of species, attracts fewer column inches, but is fundamentally serious. And poverty, the most corrosive destroyer of the environment that there is, gets hardly a mention. Poverty's twin is the extreme wealth which can afford to be careless about how it sates itself, and what damage it causes in the process. Not many parts of the media will thank you if you spend much of your time denouncing the way things are, unless you're a recognised campaigning journalist. Sustainable development? That's a phrase guaranteed to make an editor's eyes glaze over in double-quick time.

Most of us could get stories used every day if we concentrated on animals. I've sometimes felt I should be known as the correspondent for everything with big brown eyes and a wet nose. We do have to start from where people are. But part of the specialist journalist's job is to learn the skill of persuading the news editor which stories matter and which are best ignored.

If you want to be an environment journalist, it's a marvellous life. It can even involve quite a bit of foreign travel. But make sure first that you really are interested in the environment. And far more importantly, make quite sure that you really do want to be a journalist. If you're not convinced that you do, go off and do something useful instead.

Personal Profiles

Tim Hirsch - Environment Correspondent, BBC News

"I began in regional newspapers after leaving Cambridge with a degree in history, then moved to BBC Wales as a radio producer/reporter, later becoming political correspondent covering Wales from Westminster. My next move was to be BBC network news Wales correspondent, based in Cardiff. I then became one of News 24's inaugural correspondents, covering environment and transport.

It's a drawback that editors take the environment less seriously than they used to. It is a particularly fickle specialism. It's fine when it's in vogue, or if there's a big running story like foot-and-mouth. I wouldn't call myself an environmental campaigner, but I do campaign to get environmental issues onto the news agenda."

Geoffrey Lean - Environment Editor, Independent on Sunday

"I entered the field by chance when working on the Yorkshire Post. I have been an environment journalist for 32 years, 25 of them in Fleet Street. For a long time I was the only one, accustomed to meeting the entire UK green press corps in the shaving mirror each morning. I think environment journalists are an endangered species, though less so than some times in the past.

The quality dailies find they can't do without an environment specialist now, though it was different in the 1980s. There used to be active hostility then, and even now the environment is often seen as 'not real journalism'. In 2001, for the first time since 1972, environment specialists featured in the national press awards. Things like that mean our colleagues take us more seriously. And the stories have changed from the sort of 'what if' stuff we used to write to real events, like climate change and foot-and-mouth. It really is happening now."

Contacts

BBC News Online
www.bbc.co.uk

Changing Climate
www.changingclimate.org

Department for Environment, Food and Rural Affairs (DEFRA)
www.defra.gov.uk

Friends of the Earth
www.foe.co.uk

The Green Directory
www.greendirectory.net/news

Greenpeace
www.greenpeace.org.uk

International Federation of Environmental Journalists
www.ifej.org

Jobs at the BBC
www.bbc.co.uk/jobs

National Council for the Training of Journalists
www.nctj.com

National Farmers' Union
www.nfu.org.uk

National Union of Journalists
www.media.gn.apc.org/nuj.html

The Newspaper Society
www.newspapersoc.org.uk

Royal Society for the Protection Of Birds
www.rspb.org.uk/flash.html

UN Environment Programme
www.unep.org

World Wide Fund for Nature (WWF)
www.wwf-uk.org/core/index.asp

Course Listings

University of Durham

MSc in GEO-ENVIRONMENTAL ENGINEERING
A full-time, one year course comprising taught modules in Environmental Engineering, Water Engineering, Engineering Geology and Geotechnics. The focus is on practical problems relating to risk assessment and remediation of contaminated land, protection and amelioration of ground water and waste management. The taught component is complemented by a major individual project, which may be carried out in Greece, Portugal or UK.

Contact: Mrs Ann Whyatt, Secretary - Geo-Engineering, School of Engineering, University of Durham, South Road, Durham DH1 3LE, UK.
Tel: 0191374 3925; Fax: 0191374 2550
Email: Ann.Whyatt@durham.ac.uk
www.dur.ac.uk/~des0www2/Postgrad/mscs.html

University of Gloucestershire

BSc (Hons) Environmental Management
BA/BSc (Hons) Environmental Policy
BSc (Hons) Environmental Science
BA/BSc (Hons) Geography
BA (Hons) Heritage Management
BA (Hons) Landscape Management
BSc (Hons) Physical Geography
BSc (Hons) Natural Resource Management
BSc (Hons) Water Resource Management
HND Environmental Management
HND Environmental Science
MA/MSc taught programme in Environmental Policy and Management, with specialist options
MSc/MPhil/PhD by research in various environmentally-related disciplines

All programmes are available in full or part-time mode, and may be studied in different combinations, and in combinations with other subjects such as Community Development, Tourism Management, Landscape Design and Business Management. Most programmes are professionally accredited by the Institution of Environmental Sciences.

For information about undergraduate study, please contact Mike Addis (soe@glos.ac.uk). For enquiries on postgraduate study, contact Melanie Warr (mwarr@glos.ac.uk).

School of Environment, University of Gloucestershire, Francis Close Hall, Swindon Road, Cheltenham, GL50 4AZ.
Tel: +44 (0)1242 532922
Website: www.glos.ac.uk

University of Hertfordshire

The Department of Environmental Sciences at the University of Hertfordshire has been offering degrees on aspects of the environment for over 25 years.

Current programmes consider the physical, biological and social situation of humans with an emphasis on the interaction of humans with these realms of OUR environment, and the utilisation and management of resources which affect human survival and quality of life.

Our students come from throughout the United Kingdom, elsewhere in Europe and from many other overseas countries. For the undergraduate programmes, both full-time and part-time study are available; for the postgraduate programmes students may study full-time or by distance learning in the workplace. Short courses for professional up-dating are also available*.

UNDERGRADUATE DEGREES
Conservation Management
Environmental Geology
Environmental Management
Environmental Studies
Geography
Geography and Geology
Geographical Information Sciences

POSTGRADUATE DEGREES
Environmental Management for Agriculture
Environmental Management for Biodiversity and Wildlife
Environmental Management for Business
Travel and Environmental Management
Waste and Environmental Management
Water and Environmental Management

*SHORT COURSES FOR PROFESSIONAL UPDATING
Environmental Auditing
Managing Alien Invasive Weeds
GIS (a range of aspects, e.g. river and floodplain management)
Identification of Plants and Animals (e.g. freshwater invertebrates, beetles and aquatic plants)

*Courses can be tailored for specific needs

Full details of the undergraduate and postgraduate programmes including contact details can be found at:
www.herts.ac.uk/natsci/Env/ and www.herts.ac.uk/natsci/Env/envman

University of Manchester

The Institute for Development Policy and Management (IDPM) is a multidisciplinary postgraduate department of the University of Manchester.

IDPM has been awarded international excellence for our teaching and research.

IDPM offers the following annual Environmental programmes:

MSc in ENVIRONMENT AND DEVELOPMENT
12 months full time, 24 months part time

IMPACT ASSESSMENT FOR SUSTAINABLE DEVELOPMENT: INTEGRATING ENVI-RONMENTAL ASSESSMENT WITH ECONOMIC AND SOCIAL APPRAISAL.
September - December

For further information on these and our other programmes please contact:

Mrs Maggie Baldwin, Marketing and Publicity Administrator
IDPM, University of Manchester
Crawford House, Precinct Centre
Oxford Road,
MANCHESTER, M13 9GH, UK
Tel: +44 (0)161 275 2804/2800; Fax: +44 (0)161 273 8829
Email: maggie.baldwin@man.ac.uk

Brochure texts, online or downloadable application forms and other information on the work of IDPM is available at www.man.ac.uk/idpm

Masters Course in
Biology of Water Resource Management

Are you interested in the aquatic environment and do you want to work in the areas of water resource management and conservation, pollution assessment and control, or science applied to the aquatic environment?

This long-established one year full-time modular course focuses on the causes, effects and control of water pollution and the management of aquatic resources. The course offers graduates in biological sciences, environmental sciences and related disciplines the education and training necessary to enter a career in marine and freshwater resource management.

The course covers a wide range of topics with a strong emphasis on practical and field work, case studies and a 16 week, practical, work-based research project in a water management laboratory.

Eighty percent of the course's graduates are working in water resource management or closely related fields.

For further details please contact : School of Life Sciences, Napier University, 10 Colinton Road, Edinburgh EH10 5DT, tel: 0131 455 2376 or email: e.prentice@napier.ac.uk
Or visit our website at: www.lifesciences.napier.ac.uk/bwrm

NAPIER UNIVERSITY
EDINBURGH

MSc/PGDip in Environmental Assessment and Management
MSc/PGDip in Environmental Management and Technology

■ 12 months full-time, 24 months part-time ■ Good range of options ■ Inter-disciplinary teaching in natural and social sciences ■ Outstanding HEFCE-rated teaching quality ■ Bursaries available ■ Excellent post-graduation employment record

For more information contact: Elizabeth Wilson (EAM) ebwilson@brookes.ac.uk or Graham Wood (EMT) gjwood@brookes.ac.uk

MRes in Environmental Impact Assessment

■ Includes training in research methods and methodology ■ Recognised for ESRC's '1+3' funded studentships
For more information contact: Elizabeth Wilson ebwilson@brookes.ac.uk

Distance-learning Certificate in Strategic Environmental Assessment

■ CD or web-based course ■ International focus and practical application
For more information see: www.brookes.ac.uk/schools/planning/SEAmicroSEA.html

For an application form contact:
Ruth Ellis-Lay, EIA Courses Administrator, School of Planning
Oxford Brookes University, Oxford OX3 0BP

Tel: 01865 483450 Email rellis-lay@brookes.ac.uk

www.brookes.ac.uk

OXFORD
BROOKES
UNIVERSITY

Park Lane College Environmental Education Centre in Leeds

Environmental, conservation and horticulture courses from entry level to HND.

Courses combine practical skills and theory to maximise employability in the sector. Courses also include vocational qualifications (e.g. brush-cutting, chainsaw, dry stone walling etc) and you select your own specialist career pathway into the industry.

Level 1 & 2 - NVQs in Horticulture and Practical Conservation
Level 3 - National Diploma in Countryside Management & Horticulture
Level 4 - Higher National Diploma (f/t) or Certificate (p/t) in Conservation & Environmental Studies

Contact Karen Hayday or Andrew Whitehead at:
Park Lane College Environmental Education Centre, Horsforth Centre, Calverley Lane, Horsforth, Leeds LS18 4RQ
Tel: 0113 216 2400
Fax: 0113 216 2401
E-mail: course.enquiries@parklanecoll.ac.uk
www.parklanecoll.ac.uk

Sheffield Hallam University

DO YOU HAVE A FEEL FOR THE COUNTRYSIDE?
If your answer is 'yes' then we may have the course for you. We offer unique courses at both undergraduate and postgraduate level:

BSc (Hons) Environmental Conservation
BSc (Hons) Outdoor Recreation Management
MSc Environmental Management for Conservation and Recreation

and by distance learning:
MSc Outdoor Management Development
MSc Public Rights of Way and Countryside Access Management

For further information contact Lesley Merchant (Tel: 0114 225 3506) or visit our web site: www.shu.ac.uk

University of Surrey

MSc in Water and Environmental Engineering

The Centre for Environmental Health Engineering runs a modular MSc Programme which emphasises water and wastewater engineering, waste management, the protection of public health and the management of the water cycle. The Programme is suitable for engineering or science graduates and is available on a full-time or part-time basis. For further details, please contact: Olive Edwards, Tel. 01483 689532, Email: o.edwards@surrey.ac.uk, Website: http://www.surrey.ac.uk/CEHE/index.htm

MSc in Environmental Strategy

The Centre for Environmental Strategy is a multi-disciplinary postgraduate research and training centre (rated 5A in the 2001 Research Assessment Exercise). We run a flexible modular programme, available on a full or part-time basis, to develop knowledge and practical skills. Modules include Life Cycle assessment, Sustainable Development, Environmental Auditing and environmental Law. Incorporates a direct route to Associate Membership of the Institute of Environmental Management and Assessment (IEMA). Contact Penny Savill, Tel. 01483 689047, Email p.savill@surrey.ac.uk, Website http://www.surrey.ac.uk/eng/ces

University of Surrey, Guildford, Surrey GU2 7XH

ADC Environment

are the
publishers of this book for CIWEM.
Tel: 01268 450024

We are also publishers of:

www.environmentpost.co.uk

www.greendirectory.net

Glossary

AMP	Asset Management Plan
BAP	Biodiversity Action Plan
BEng	Bachelor of Engineering
BSc	Bachelor of Science
BSI	British Standards Institute
BTCV	British Trust for Conservation Volunteers
BTEC	A series of qualifications available from the awarding body Edexcel
BW	British Waterways
CA	Countryside Agency
CAD	Computer Aided Design
CAP	Common Agricultural Policy
CCW	Countryside Council for Wales
CEE	Council for Environmental Education
CEFAS	Centre for Environment, Fisheries and Aquaculture Science
CIWEM	Chartered Institution of Water and Environmental Management
CIWM	Chartered Institution of Wastes Management
CPD	Continuing Professional Development
CV	Curriculum Vitae
DARD	Department of Agriculture and Rural Development (Northern Ireland)
DEFRA	Department for Environment, Food and Rural Affairs
DFID	Department for International Development
DOENI	Department of the Environment in Northern Ireland
DTI	Department of Trade and Industry
DWI	Drinking Water Inspectorate
EA	Environment Agency (for England and Wales)
EC	European Community (now known as EU - see below)
EHO	Environmental Health Officer
EIA	Environmental Impact Assessment
EMAS	Eco-Management and Audit Scheme
EMS	Environmental Management System
ENDS	Environmental Data Services
EPA	Environment Protection Assistant
EPO	Environment Protection Officer
ERDF	European Regional Development Fund
ESD	Education for Sustainable Development
EU	European Union
FC	Forestry Commission
FWAG	Farming and Wildlife Advisory Group
GIS	Geographical Information System
GPS	Global Positioning Systems

HLF	Heritage Lottery Fund
HNC/D	Higher National Certificate/Diploma
ICE	Institution of Civil Engineers
IEMA	Institute of Environmental Management and Assessment
IFM	Institute of Fisheries Management
IPC	Integrated Pollution Control
IPPC	Integrated Pollution Prevention and Control
ISO14001	Internationally recognised standard for Environmental Management Systems (EMS)
IT	Information Technology
IWA	Inland Waterways Association
LA21	Local Agenda 21
MEng	Master of Engineering
MSc	Master of Science
NFU	National Farmers' Union
NGO	Non-Governmental Organisation
NRA	National Rivers Authority
NSCA	National Society for Clean Air and Environmental Protection
OFWAT	Office of Water Services
ONC/D	Ordinary National Certificate/Diploma
PFI	Private Finance Initiative
PhD	Doctor of Philosophy
PIG	Pipeline Industries Guild
R&D	Research and Development
RICS	Royal Institution of Chartered Surveyors
RSPB	Royal Society for the Protection of Birds
RTPI	Royal Town Planning Institute
SEPA	Scottish Environment Protection Agency
SiLC	Specialist in Land Contamination
SOAEFD	Scottish Office Agriculture Environment & Fisheries Department
SSSI	Site of Special Scientific Interest
SUDS	Sustainable Urban Drainage Systems
VSO	Voluntary Service Overseas
WAMITAB	Waste Management Industry Training and Advisory Board
WFD	Water Framework Directive
WRc	Water Research Centre

Index

NOTES